THE VIRUSES

The Natural History Press, publisher for The American Museum of Natural History, is a division of Doubleday & Company, Inc. Directed by a joint editorial board made up of members of the staff of both the Museum and Doubleday, The Natural History Press publishes books and periodicals in all branches of the life and earth sciences, including anthropology and astronomy. The Natural History Press has its editorial offices at The American Museum of Natural History, Central Park West at 79th Street, New York 24, New York, and its business offices at 501 Franklin Avenue, Garden City, New York.

THE VIRUSES

Helena Curtis

Published for
The American Museum of Natural History

The Natural History Press
Garden City, New York

To Sally and Mark

Acknowledgments

I am grateful for the kind personal assistance of Drs. Igor Tamm, Peyton Rous, and Richard E. Shope of The Rockefeller Institute; Drs. Frank L. Horsfall, Jr., and Charlotte Friend of the Sloan-Kettering Institute; Drs. Max Delbrück and Robert S. Edgar of the California Institute of Technology; and Dr. Pierre Nicolle of the Pasteur Institute in Paris. But all errors in the book are, of course, entirely my own.

H.C.

The line illustrations for this book were prepared by the Graphic Arts Division of The American Museum of Natural History. The photographs were supplied by The American Museum of Natural History unless otherwise acknowledged.

Contents

ILLUSTRATIONS

Figures

Part I

THE BEGINNINGS

1 "For Life Is a Germ . . ."

At some point in time, once man had learned to walk erect and clutch a sharpened stone, he began to wonder. It was at this moment, of which no fossil trace remains, that he became different from all the other animals. Poetry was born then, religion, science, philosophy, and all the other awesome joys and fears that are our heritage.

This one story of man's wondering is about viruses. Viruses are, of course, the agents of ugly disease, and there are rational and humanitarian reasons for man to use his intelligence, his special adaptation, to understand and so control them. Yet, side by side with these reasons, close but completely separate, there exists the unquenchable, inexplicably simple desire for knowledge for its own sake. And these are the two themes of this book.

To the scientist, the wonderer, viruses have become again and again a focus of certain key questions in biology. Since the moment of their discovery, they have hovered, as they hover to this day, on the border line of whatever is meant by life, provoking thought, crowding definitions, and stirring controversies. The simplest forms of "living" things, or the most biologically competent forms of the "non-living," they serve as tools for probing the nature of genetics, immunology, enzymology, and cancer, which are, as a result, also the subjects of this book. Indeed, from this point of view, viruses become one way, a very elegant way, of looking at modern biology.

Historically speaking, this question of the living and the non-living seems to have concerned man for at least as long as he has left records of his thoughts behind him. Aristotle, one of the greatest of the early observers, believed that simple creatures such as worms, beetles, lice, frogs, and salamanders could originate spontaneously in dust or mud—from all dry things which become moist and all moist things that become dry. "Nature," he concluded, some 2000 years ago, "proceeds little by little from things lifeless to animal life in such a way that it is impossible to determine the exact line of demarcation nor on which side thereof an intermediate form would lie."

Paracelsus, van Helmont, and other famous physicians reported personal observations on the genesis of frogs and mice and other living creatures from a variety of inert raw materials. The Italian scientist Buonanni described a type of timberwood that, after rotting in the sea, produced worms which engendered butterflies which became birds. Such findings failed to surprise a populace that was well accustomed to the notion that rodents arose from grain, snakes from a woman's hair dropped in rain water, and plant lice from the dewdrop.

Francesco Redi of seventeenth-century Tuscany was the first to challenge spontaneous generation by experimental methods. In his most famous demonstration, he showed that maggots do not form in decaying meat unless flies lay their eggs in it. Redi's experiments deserve to be remembered because they were so carefully controlled; he used snake, fish meat, and milk-fed veal and placed them in wide-mouthed jars, some of which were open, some closed, and some covered with a fine Naples veil. Maggots appeared in the open jars but not the closed ones, and, on the jars covered with the veil, Redi was able to see the flies, attracted by the meat, depositing their eggs on the filmy material. In his book *Experiments on the Generation of Insects*, Redi traced the life cycles, some of them very complex, of a number of insect forms. So, over the years, naturalists came to know the histories of the beings of the visible world, and the fantasies of their creation were laid to rest.

But, even as these careful studies went forward, vigorous support for spontaneous generation arose from a new quarter—the early microscopists. Perhaps eels do not come from ooze, nor worms from putrefaction, but it is only necessary to put decomposing substances for a short time in a warm place and tiny "live beasts" appear under the lens before one's very eyes. Needham, a Catholic priest of Ireland, published reports in 1749, declaring that many different kinds of infusions invariably gave rise to animalcules, even though the material was first boiled to destroy all living things. His contemporary, the famous French naturalist Georges de Buffon, uneasy at these conclusions, offered a compromise: all living material, he proposed, consists of organic molecules that do not change. When a dead organism decomposes, the material of which it is formed recombines, creating new living organisms.

The Abbé Lazzaro Spallanzani, one of the greatest of the early experimenters, rejoined vigorously that life could never be generated from non-living materials. He devised elaborate experiments to demonstrate that no living animalcula ever appeared in a concoction in which they had been killed by boiling and which were sealed to prevent further entry of micro-organisms. These experimental proofs did not win over his determined opponents. His results were not always reproducible. Some micro-organisms—the spores of certain bacteria—are heat resistant. Carelessness compounded and recompounded the problems as others tried similar experiments. Further, the proponents of spontaneous generation maintained that the experiments did not prove anything anyway. Excessive heating destroyed the life forces, they argued, and drove from the flasks the oxygen needed for life. In 1858, Felix Archimede Pouchet, director of the Museum of Natural History in Rouen, read before the Paris Academy of Sciences a paper in which he claimed to have produced spontaneous generation at will by admitting air to sterilized "putrescible" materials.

Pouchet's claims produced a great sensation in scientific circles and the controversy spread, taking on philosophical overtones. The Church felt as though some matter of principle was involved, but was not sure on which side its spiritual interests lay. The situation was such that in 1860 the Academy offered a prize for carefully conducted experiments which would throw new light on the question of the so-called spontaneous generations, and Louis Pasteur put himself in contention.

When Pasteur first expressed his interest in the problem, his sponsor and mentor, Jean Baptiste Biot, demanded anxiously that he avoid these researches, warning, "You will never find your way out." But Pasteur, fresh from his studies on fermentation and the diseases of wine, realized that the question of spontaneous generation was not merely an abstraction but had a direct and pertinent relationship to the varied activities of micro-organisms, the "infinitely small," which he was coming so deeply to respect. Pasteur wisely focused on the solitary

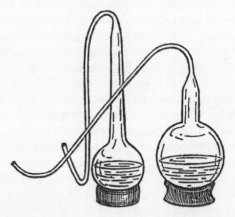

Figure 1. The swanneck flasks of Louis Pasteur.

issue of the source of the micro-organisms in infusions. His experiments were beautifully simple. Using the now famous swanneck flasks, he boiled the organic fluids his opponents claimed capable of producing life, driving air from the flasks by the boiling. Air that re-entered the flasks through the necks was filtered by the moisture collected in the narrow convolutions and no life appeared in the liquid. If the necks were broken off, micro-organisms would appear, their life starting at the precise spots where bits of dust fell upon the surface of the liquid, or if the flasks were tipped, so that the liquid touched the dust that was trapped in the necks, micro-organisms again entered the flasks. Pasteur carried sealed flasks containing yeast infusion to the Swiss Alps on muleback and opened them there, permitting the clean glacial air to rush in, and then resealed them. Most of these flasks remained sterile—and still remain so after a century—but flasks similarly filled with city air promptly showed microscopic growth. It was neither the molecules in the liquid nor the oxygen in the air nor a combination of them, but only living organisms from which other organisms could appear.

On April 7, 1864, Pasteur presented his swanneck flasks to "a scientific evening" at the Sorbonne. His public was a brilliant one, including not only professors and students but writers, artists, and members of royalty—George Sand, Dumas père, Princess Mathilde—*tout Paris*, for in those days science was neither man's servant nor his master but a delight and adornment of the cultivated mind. Pasteur's eloquence soared to the occasion:

"And therefore, gentlemen, I could point to that liquid and say to you, I have taken my drop of water from the immensity of creation and I have taken it full of the elements appropriated to the development of inferior beings. And I wait, I watch, I question it!—begging it to recommence for me the beautiful spectacle of the first creation. But it is dumb, dumb since these experiments were begun several years ago; it is dumb because I have kept it from the only thing man does not know how to produce: from the germs which float in the air, from Life, for Life is a germ and a germ is Life. Never will the doctrine of spontaneous generation recover from the mortal blow of this simple experiment."*

That was a fantastic moment in the history of biology. The literate world had been set astir by the discussions raging over Charles Darwin's *Origin of Species*. And even as Pasteur worked with the swanneck flasks, the smooth and wrinkled, green and yellow peas were being counted in the quiet monastery garden in Brunn. In the same remarkable decade, in the famed laboratories of Hoppe-Seyler in Tübingen, the Swiss biochemist Friedrich Miescher extracted an unusual substance from cells which, since it came from the nucleus, he gave the name nucleic acid. So, like the tiny specks which fell unnoticed upon the liquid in the flasks, the invisible germs of today's biology were being sown.

Pasteur's experiments marked the transition. They came at a time when botanists were marveling over the bacteria their microscopes revealed, while physicians, helpless at the bedsides of their patients, were arguing the nature of contagion. Now the ancient fallacies, the turtle breeding mud, the miasmas, humors, and demons that had ordered the course of medicine for so many centuries began to vanish, never to be seen again. Before the close of the century, most of the major bacterial agents of disease were discovered and described and many could be prevented.

Virology was born in this setting as an unwanted child of bacteriology. Robert Koch had laid down the rules for the new science: before one could assume that a disease was caused by a micro-organism, he counseled, one must first show its presence in every instance of the disease; second, one must isolate and cultivate it in a pure medium; and, finally, one must reinject it into the animal and reproduce the disease.

Viruses did not abide by the rules. John Brown Buist,

* This is taken from René Dubos' magnificent biography, *Louis Pasteur, Free Lance of Science*.

in 1887, searching for the cause of smallpox, removed material from pox, stained the cells, and was able to demonstrate, regularly, the appearance of tiny granules in the cell body. He was unable to isolate and grow them, however, so he abandoned the problem, and decades passed before their nature was understood. Pasteur searched in vain for a causative bacteria in the blood and tissues of dogs with rabies. When he did not find one, he characteristically pushed on to step three and grew the agent, whatever it was, in the nervous tissue of living animals and developed a vaccine. But the unruly diseases were sources of discontent in this golden age of bacteriology.

Sometimes it was not clear whether a disease was caused by bacterial cells themselves or by a toxin or some other substance in the medium. One of the ways for studying this was to collect the bacterial cells in a filter and to see whether they or the fluid from which they had been isolated held the noxious powers. In 1892, Dmitri Iwanowski, a Russian, presented a brief scientific paper on tobacco mosaic disease, a common condition that mottles tobacco leaves and makes them brittle. Tobacco mosaic, then as now, was proving a source of crop loss to farmers in the Crimea as well as in other parts of the world. Iwanowski noted that the sap from the infected plants retained its infectious qualities even after it passed through the filter, but this observation went largely unnoticed, and Iwanowski did no further work on the subject.

The crucial experiment was performed in 1898 by a Dutch botanist, Martinus Beijerinck. Beijerinck, a specialist in plant diseases, had tried twice before without success to isolate the organism that caused tobacco mosaic disease. On this third occasion, he forced the fluid through a fine filter and discovered, as had Iwanowski, that it was the filtered fluid that produced the disease. Then he found that the juice of the leaf which had been infected by the filtrate could itself yield a filtrate that would induce the disease in another healthy plant. The filtrate was not merely a toxin or poison but seemed to have a continuing life of its own. Since Beijerinck could find nothing in the fluid, search as he would, and could cultivate nothing from the fluid, he concluded that it was the fluid itself that produced the infection, *contagium vivum fluidum* he called it.

Somewhat later Beijerinck wrote: "The existence of these contagia proves that the concept of life—if one considers metabolism and proliferation as its essential characters—is not inseparably linked with that of structure; the criteria of life . . . are also compatible with the fluid state. . . . In its most primitive form life is, therefore, no longer bound to the cell. . . . In its primitive form life is like a fire, like a flame borne by the living substance—like a flame which appears in endless diversity and yet has specificity within it . . . which does not originate by spontaneous generation but is propagated by another flame."

In the same year, 1898, Friedrich Loeffler and Paul Frosch published a more prosaic account, describing the transmission of foot-and-mouth disease in cattle by a cell-free filtrate by means of a serum that had been passed through a filter capable of retaining the smallest known bacteria. So, on these two notes, virology began.

2   The Ultramicrobe

In the earliest studies of the infectious diseases, man was his own laboratory and his own test tube. He watched and worried and by trial and error—and in these experiments error is often just another way of saying death—learned measures to protect himself and his fellows. The leper of Biblical times was made to cry, "Unclean, unclean," to warn others of his presence. Centuries later, a yellow jack was flown from infected ships to warn healthy ones to keep their distance. It came to be known that even seemingly well people might carry disease. Persons were not allowed to flee a plague-ridden city for fear they might take the plague with them. The word "quarantine" echoes the forty days a ship had to wait before discharging passengers at Venice. "Contagion" itself, used by the ancients, comes from the Latin word *contagio*, "to touch," which carries with it the notion that diseases spread from man to man.

These ideas were not clear and coherent, however. They explained so little. Why did an epidemic sweep down like a fury and disappear as mysteriously as it had come? Why was one village decimated, another spared? Why would all the children from one household be taken, and none from a neighbor's? So, while some diseases were thought to be spread from person to person, others were attributed to bad air—the *miasmas*—or to Acts of Providence, or they were regarded as the fruits of unusual sins. There were speculations on the presence of invisible animalcules in the air long before Anthony van Leeuwenhoek saw the first "monsters" through his microscope. On the other hand, as late as 1793 the great Benjamin Rush attributed the Philadelphia yellow-fever epidemic to "damaged coffee which had putrefied on a wharf near Arch Street." Less than 100 years ago, Florence Nightingale scoffed at the idea that there were specific disease-causing organisms that propagated themselves ". . . like a dog or a cat. There are no specific diseases," she said, "there are specific disease conditions"; by which she meant poverty, filth, and malnutrition, those faithful bedfellows of infection. At about the same time in Vienna, Ignaz Semmelweis died defeated and insane, still trying to persuade his colleagues that their unclean hands and clothing were spreading childbed fever.

Smallpox was the most effective of the early teachers. Many of the infectious diseases could not be clearly distinguished from one another, but smallpox left its unmistakable signature. The pox was an ancient plague. It was probably introduced into Europe by the Crusaders and by the Saracens when they invaded Spain. It flourished and spread until, by the eighteenth century, smallpox haunted the streets of the big cities. One in ten persons died of the disease, and ninety-five per cent of Europeans who survived their childhood had had it. About half were left permanently scarred and many were blinded. Young women studied their reflections in the mirror, waiting their inevitable turn. They learned to scratch their legs and feet at the first sign of the disease, in the knowledge that the ugly pox would then localize in these decorously concealed locations and so, perhaps, spare their faces and bosoms. No one could miss the fact that a person who had suffered an attack was almost never stricken again. Pox scars were required of domestic servants, particularly of nursemaids, as the prime certificate of employability.

It came to be recognized that some epidemics of smallpox were more severe than others, and that, since one had to have the disease, it was advantageous to be able to choose when to have it. Intentional infection of children with material preserved from a mild epidemic had long been practiced in the Far East. The Chinese used powdered scabs, "heavenly flowers," as snuff. The Arabs carried matter from smallpox pustules around in nutshells and injected it under the skin on the point of a needle.

Variolation, as the Europeans called smallpox inoculation, was introduced into England in 1717 by Lady Mary Wortley Montagu, wife of the British Ambassador to Turkey. The deliberately caused disease was usually mild and had a low mortality, although it was as contagious as normally contracted smallpox, and variolation is believed responsible for some epidemics of the pox. Variolation became a stock in trade with the barber surgeons and, by 1746, a Hospital for the Inoculation against Smallpox had been established for the poor of London where they could be confined during the course of induced infection.

Edward Jenner, an English country doctor, was impressed by the conviction of the country people that a person who had had cowpox, a mild disease of farm animals that sometimes affected man, was immune to smallpox. Jenner tried variolation on several persons who had had cowpox and was unable to induce any infection in them. Emboldened, in 1796 he inoculated a boy with fluid taken from a pustule on the hand of a milkmaid with cowpox and subsequently demonstrated that the boy was immune to variolation and so, presumably, to smallpox. By 1800, at least 100,000 persons had been vaccinated, and the smallpox, man's hideous companion for so many centuries, lost its hold on the western world.

Jenner had believed that smallpox and cowpox were related—in fact, in his famous monograph he called cowpox *variolae vaccinae*, smallpox of cows—but, beyond that, there seems to have been no speculation on why vaccination worked, and for decades no one attempted to immunize against another disease.

In 1879, Pasteur and his colleagues had just isolated

the causative bacteria of chicken cholera when their work was interrupted by summer vacation. When they returned, they discovered that the cultures that had been stored over the summer months were no longer infectious when injected into chickens. They isolated a fresh strain of the cholera and used it to inoculate a group of chickens which included those used in the previous experiment. Unlike the other members of the group, these chickens did not contract the disease.

Pasteur realized quickly—"chance favors only the prepared mind"—that he had rediscovered in the laboratory the principles of Jenner's immunization for smallpox and, to emphasize the relationship, proposed that the term vaccination be used for all immunization procedures in which a related but weaker organism was used to confer immunity against its more virulent relative. In the three years following this accidental discovery, Pasteur had developed practical vaccines against chicken cholera, anthrax, and swine erysipelas, all bacterial infections, and had begun to turn his attention to rabies.

Rabies

Rabies differs from other viral diseases of man in being the only known virus that is fatal in every case in which infection is established. It is also unusual among the "classic" viruses for its long incubation period. Although uncommon in Pasteur's time, as it is today, rabies was greatly feared, and Pasteur was known and revered throughout France more for his "conquest" of rabies than for all the rest of his astonishing catalogue of contributions to biology and medicine.

When Pasteur first began to study rabies, he was discomfited by not being able to find the causative organism, much less to culture it outside the living host. He and his assistant, Emile Roux, were able to surmount the problem of maintaining the organism, which they col-

lected from the saliva of captured rabid dogs, by passing
it from dog to dog, inoculating it right into the brain.
They found that it would also grow, following intracerebral inoculation, in monkeys, guinea pigs, and rabbits. By rabbit passage, Pasteur developed what he called
a "fixed" virus (virus at this time was a term generally
applied to any disease-causing agent or poison), one
which would kill the rabbits regularly and in exactly six
days, whereas "street" viruses, strains isolated fresh from
captured animals, were far more wayward in their effects.

The vaccine Pasteur finally developed, after long trial
and error, was prepared from the isolated spinal cords of
rabbits that had died from the fixed virus. Unlike cowpox,
even this attenuated virus was far too virulent to be given
in a single dose, but, remembering from his previous
studies that gradual exposure of sheep to small doses of
anthrax may build up an immunity, Pasteur inoculated
dogs over a two-week period with increasingly virulent
emulsions of infected spinal cord until, by the fourteenth
day, they were immune to injections of full-strength prep-
arations and to all subsequent challenge with rabies. In
dogs as well as in man, the disease develops slowly, and
for this reason Pasteur struck upon the unorthodox idea
that it might be possible to establish immunity after infection, during the long incubation period of the disease.
This was successfully accomplished in dogs under experimental conditions, but neither Pasteur himself nor Roux
nor the medical profession at large felt inclined to inoculate a human being with rabies.

In July 1885, nine-year-old Joseph Meister was brought
to Pasteur from Alsace. He had been attacked two days
before and had deep, multiple bites that, in the opinion
of all physicians consulted, made rabies infection inevitable. Under Pasteur's supervision, the boy was given twelve
successive inoculations of increasingly virulent material
until, on the last day, he received a full-strength dose of
the fixed virus.

Meister never showed any symptoms from either the bites or the injections. He became gatekeeper of the Pasteur Institute and in 1940, when the Nazi Army invaded Paris and ordered him to open Pasteur's crypt, the sixty-four-year-old Meister committed suicide rather than obey, keeping faith as best he could with a man who had risked his reputation to save the life of an unknown child.

By the end of 1886, some 2500 persons had received Pasteur's rabies vaccines, although the cause of rabies, as of smallpox, still remained unknown.

Yellow Jack

The first virus disease of man was not identified until the twentieth century when Walter Reed induced yellow fever in human beings with a cell-free filtrate. Yellow jack itself was not new. It had stalked the Atlantic trade routes for 300 years, from Africa to South America, through the Caribbean and around the Gulf ports, up the Mississippi and down the Amazon, with seasonal excursions as far north as London and Boston, leaving fear and death in its wake. The legends of the ghost ships, *The Flying Dutchman* and *The Rime of the Ancient Mariner*, may well have had their origin on sea lanes where yellow fever sailed.

Following a number of deaths from yellow fever of American soldiers in Cuba during the Spanish-American War, a United States Army Commission was established to study the disease and sent to Cuba under Major Reed in 1900. Failing to isolate the presumed bacterial cause of the disease and seeking other approaches to the problem, Reed, like Jenner before him, took advantage of local knowledge. Twenty years earlier, Dr. Carlos J. Finlay of Havana had formally proposed that yellow fever was carried by a mosquito. Reed talked to Finlay, who described his evidence and also gave him the mosquito eggs from which were hatched the insect colony with which the

Commission's experiments were performed. By September 1900, Reed's group had recorded three cases of yellow fever transmitted by mosquitoes that had fed upon patients with the disease. By September 1901, yellow fever, which had not left Havana for more than 150 years, completely vanished, never to return again.

The findings of the Commission were remarkably clearcut. Yellow fever was not passed by contaminated clothing, bad air, nor contact with other patients, but only by the bite of a mosquito. The infectious agent was in the blood for the first three days of the fever; in other words, if a patient were protected from mosquitoes during this period, he could not transmit the disease. The mosquito could not infect another person for twelve days after he had taken the blood of the yellow-fever patient; this delay was the cause of the failure by Finlay and other investigators to demonstrate conclusively that the disease was mosquito-borne. This amount of time is required, it is now known, for the virus to multiply in the body of the insect and travel to the salivary glands, from which it is injected into each new mosquito-bite victim during the insect's life, which may be as long as two or three months.

William H. Welch of Johns Hopkins called Reed's attention to the account by Loeffler and Frosch on the transmission of foot-and-mouth disease in cattle by a filtrate. Reed injected diluted filtered serum from a patient into three volunteers, two of whom came down with yellow fever. Despite Reed's unequivocal results, almost thirty years passed before the search for a yellow-fever bacterium was relinquished and the viral cause widely accepted.

The mosquito that carried yellow fever in Havana was *Aëdes aegypti*, a species that dwelt in and around human habitations, breeding in rain barrels and other open containers of water (in which, of course, it could also make ocean voyages). It often remained in one dwelling and even in one room for all of its life, hiding in corners and

rafters, not even humming to warn of its presence. On
the basis of the report of Reed's Commission, Major William C. Gorgas, Chief Sanitary Officer in Havana, took
measures against the mosquito, covering water containers
or pouring a film of oil on them and spraying and screening the dwellings of newly infected patients. It was relatively simple to break the tenuous chain of infection.
From Havana, Gorgas went to Panama and, by the same
measures, drove *Aëdes aegypti* and its deadly passenger
from the Canal Zone.

The total eradication of yellow fever was not so simple.
Pockets of the disease continued throughout the world.
In 1916 the newly formed Rockefeller Foundation created
a Commission on Yellow Fever, under General Gorgas,
to eliminate the last remnants of disease before it could
be spread through the new trade routes opening as a
result of the completion of the Panama Canal. In the
1920s it was discovered that, in addition to the urban
yellow fever carried from man to man, there was a jungle
type of fever, found both in Africa and South America
and transmitted from monkey to monkey, and sometimes
to other animals, by a number of strains of mosquito. In
this cycle, man was not a necessary component, but those
who worked on the edge of the jungle or pushed into its
interior might fall accidental victims and initiate a new
man-mosquito-man chain of infection. Yellow fever still
lives in the jungle and probably always will but there are
now vaccines to protect against it.

Growth of Virology

During these initial thirty years following the discovery
of the first viral disease of man, little was learned of the
nature of viruses. They were studied almost entirely in
terms of their effects. In patients, diagnoses were based
on symptoms. In the laboratory, identification of a virus
depended on the injection of something invisible into

a suitable host, if one could be found, and waiting to see what happened. The amount of the virus was estimated in terms of how much a sample could be diluted, or titrated, in the language of the laboratory, before its infectivity was lost.

By this time it was known that the sera of animals, including people, who had recovered from infections contained substances that combined very specifically with the particular infecting agent and neutralized it. These substances, which were given the name of antibodies, served to prevent second attacks of many infectious diseases. Most important for the study of viruses, it was found that antibodies, because they are so highly specific, could be used to identify viruses. Simply by injecting an animal (the rabbit is most useful) with a known agent, it is possible to produce substances that will clearly identify this agent on all other encounters.

The symptoms produced by virus, it also came to be recognized, resulted secondarily from the damage done to the specific tissues the viruses attacked. Yellow-fever virus, for example, after it is injected into the skin by a mosquito, goes through a round of multiplication in the adjacent lymph nodes and then, optionally, a second round in the heart, liver, and other internal organs. It is this second round that produces the typical "sulky pulse," jaundice, and gastric hemorrhages—*vomito negro* —which are the characteristic triad of this disease. Viruses which affect the skin also multiply in two waves, first internally, often in the lymphoid tissue, and secondly in the skin, to form the typical rash or pox. Rabies virus and polio multiply in special cells of the central nervous system, so producing paralysis. Influenza and the common cold, on the other hand, multiply in the surface cells of the respiratory tract, resulting in the all-too-familiar mucous discharge from these areas.

In 1928, *Filterable Viruses* appeared, the first of a number of classic texts by Thomas Rivers of The Rockefeller

Institute for Medical Research. Rivers, dean and arbiter of this tumultuous new science for thirty years, brought the field into focus, giving form to the sporadically accumulated data, discarding the irrelevant and the unproven, and so establishing virology as a respectable and recognized subdivision of bacteriology. He stressed that viruses were parasites, differing from most, although not all, other agents of infection in that they were able to multiply only in the presence of living tissue. In subsequent editions of his book, the word "filterable" was dropped, and thus "virus" had completed its etymological journey from a word meaning any infectious poison to the quite precise meaning that it has today.

In 1929 and 1930, important advances were made in the technique of handling viruses. First, Howard B. Andervont of the Public Health Service showed that herpes simplex, the virus that causes fever blisters, could be grown in the most convenient of laboratory animals, the mouse, if it were inoculated by intracerebral injection, the method used by Pasteur and Roux. Max Theiler of Harvard then succeeded in transmitting yellow-fever virus to mice by intracerebral injection, an advance that led directly to the first yellow-fever vaccine. In the next year Ernest Goodpasture of Vanderbilt University established a viral infection in a fertilized hen's egg, one of the most perfect and least expensive biological containers known. From this time on, laboratory work with a number of viruses became possible.

In 1931, William J. Elford of the National Institute for Medical Research in England succeeded in developing a series of extremely fine graded filters. He was thus able to show that a virus could go through one filter but would be caught in another. From 1931 to 1935, Elford and his group studied most of the viruses for which animal hosts were available and showed that each type had a characteristic size, which actually he was able to estimate with remarkable accuracy. Now, although viruses had not been seen, it was known once and for all that they were particulate in nature, not a living fluid, and that, like other organisms, they have their own specific sizes and probably their own shapes also. So the viruses at last assumed a comfortable and respectable status, differing from the bacteria in certain regards, but in no way challenging man to seek new definitions of "life" or to make room for exceptions within the old.

Then in 1935 there came an announcement so incomprehensible that many refused to believe it for years. Biochemistry during the early 1930s was much concerned with proteins. Three of the body's enzymes, urease, trypsin, and pepsin, had just been isolated, purified, and proved, to a skeptical scientific public, to consist solely of giant protein molecules. An important part of the proof that enzymes were pure protein was that they were obtained in a crystalline form, for crystals are made up of identical molecules, each of which attaches to the other until the mass grows finally into a shape specified by the structure of the molecule itself.

In one of those extraordinary flashes of illogical inspiration that contribute as much to science as the slow patient accumulation of knowledge one hears so much about, Wendell Stanley, a young biochemist at the Princeton laboratory of The Rockefeller Institute, set out to characterize a virus chemically. He chose tobacco mosaic, the virus of Beijerinck, because it was stable under a variety of conditions and safe to work with, and because the characteristic infection could be demonstrated easily and rapidly. In 1935, from the juice squeezed from a ton of tobacco leaves, Stanley was able to extract the first sample of pure virus. Then he showed that if this virus were isolated under certain conditions, it formed readily visible needle-like crystals. (See Plate 1.) It could be kept in this form indefinitely. The virus was not a small bacterium. It was a molecule, a pure crystalline substance.

But when these crystals were put back into solution,

they once more became infective, acquiring the classic properties of activity, hereditary continuity, and self-replication; in other words, these shimmering needles, these inert molecules, became alive, just like the lady's hair dropped in the rain barrel. As Rivers said, the virus was either "organule" or "molechism," with the line of demarcation between the living and the non-living too fine to be drawn.

3   The Cancer Viruses

The "virus theory of cancer" is almost as old as virology itself. In 1903 Amedée Borrell, noting that the pox viruses made cells proliferate, speculated that viruses might one day prove to be a cause of cancer. In 1908 Wilhelm Ellerman and Olaf Bang reported that fowl leukosis, a type of leukemia common in chickens, could be transmitted by a filterable virus. The leukemias and lymphomas—diseases of the blood-forming tissues—were not recognized as members of the cancer family in those days, and this discovery did not cause so much as a ripple in the mainstream of cancer research.

The next year a breeder of Plymouth Rock hens noticed a tumor in the breast of one of his chickens and thought the animal might be of some interest to cancer research. The first two laboratories to which he offered the animal turned him away, but he finally found a young scientist, newly interested in the cancer problem, who would accept the contribution. By this coincidence, Peyton Rous, another "prepared mind," encountered the sarcoma that now, half a century later, is still a storm center of research in the cancer virus field.

Rous transplanted the cancer successfully through several generations to other hens of the Plymouth Rock strain. In cases in which the graft took, it grew slowly and deliberately, usually first attaining a large size and then beginning to spread to other parts of the animal, eventually causing its death. Rous was a pathologist by training and was able to establish clearly that the chicken sarcoma both looked and acted like a typical cancer, points that proved important in the long controversy that followed. After a series of successful transplants of the cancer, Rous, aware of the work of Ellerman and Bang, ground up some sarcoma tissue, passed it through a fine filter, and injected the fluid into other hens of the Plymouth Rock strain. As he reported in 1911, the cell-free filtrate (years passed before Rous called it a virus) produced the same characteristic slow-growing fibrous sarcoma that had been seen in the animals in which direct transplants of cancer tissue had been made.

The notion that any form of cancer was caused by a virus was not a comfortable one. The long fight against the prejudice that cancer was a contagious disease was just drawing to a close; this belief had kept cancer patients out of general hospitals as late as the turn of the century, and physicians were anxious to avoid any return or even reminder of this sad epoch in medical history. Laboratory investigators, also, were still suffering from the enthusiasms of the early bacteriologists who had isolated one bacterium after another from cancer tissue and proclaimed each to be cause of the disease. This now was the great era of classic pathology. Attention was focused on the cell. The many different forms of cancer were described and classified at this time and the skills of microscopic diagnosis of cancer were being developed. Cancer was generally thought to be a result of a change in the genetic make-up of a cell; in support of this theory was the accumulating evidence that agents such as X-rays, ultraviolet light, and certain chemicals that caused mutations in lower organisms, such as fruit flies, were carcinogenic in higher animals. The intellectual climate was not favorable for a cancer virus.

The few who continued to work with the Rous sarcoma virus made some very interesting discoveries, however. Rous found that the virus tended to localize at a point of injury; the whole chicken could be flooded with virus, but the tumor would appear just at the spot where the injection needle had broken the skin. Or if this area was immediately sterilized or cauterized so the virus would not grow there, and a slight injury was induced elsewhere in the chicken's body, the characteristic cancer would appear at the site of the induced injury, not unlike the pox which would appear in the self-induced scratches on the legs of the European ladies. Antibodies to the virus could be found in the blood stream of the host, but they did not affect the growth of the tumor. There was, as Rous put it, some special and clandestine relationship between the virus and the tumor cell.

Francisco Duran-Reynals of Yale found that age was an important factor in the type of disease that the virus induced. In the adult chicken, the virus caused the typical slow-growing sarcoma that would slowly spread, or metastasize, to other parts of the body. In the newborn chick, however, the virus did not cause cell proliferation but rather cell destruction, resulting in a rapidly fatal hemorrhagic disease.

Also, with the Rous virus, the amount of tumor and its rate of growth parallel the amount of virus in the inoculum. With most virus infections, one either gets the disease or not, and the severity of a case of measles and the number of spots on one's face do not have anything to do with the size of the infecting dose. But with the Rous virus, as it has been carefully calculated by W. Ray Bryan at the National Cancer Institute, tumors appear in five or six days following a strong dose of virus while, if a weaker dose is given, it may take several weeks for the cancer to develop.

Often, particularly in the early experiments, infectious virus could not be recovered at all from the tumor, which added fuel to the flames of the controversy. The virus was not a true virus, they cried, the sarcoma not a true sarcoma, the filter not a true filter, the chicken was not a respectable laboratory animal—and the Rous sarcoma was only an academic curiosity.

Fowl Leukemias

In a slightly different atmosphere, work continued on the leukemias and lymphomas of the fowl. These posed a severe economic problem in the poultry industry. It was established that a whole group of cancers of the blood-forming tissues in fowl are closely related; chickens inoculated with cell-free filtrates from an animal with one of the diseases form antibodies active against the viruses of the other leukemias or lymphomas; apparently they are all strains of the same virus family which investigators now term the avian leukemia complex. Ellerman discovered that antibodies to the avian leukemia viruses also, surprisingly, neutralize the Rous sarcoma virus, which strongly suggested that this agent also belongs to the same virus family.

At least one of these strains of fowl leukemia is definitely contagious. It is passed from mother to chick through the egg, and chicks can spread it from one to another through saliva and droppings. Many of the animals do not develop leukemia, although they harbor the virus all of their lives; poultry shippers face a constant problem of whether to deliver infected resistant chickens that will probably not develop leukemia, but will infect the poultryman's healthy flocks, or virus-free chickens who may well pick up a fatal disease from the farmer's own stock. The problem was of great interest to veterinary medicine, but it appeared to bear very little relationship to human disease.

Papillomas

The wart, on the contrary, is a human disease so common to man as to be the subject of much folklore. At one time, before youth became so sophisticated, warts were known to be caused by handling toads, as any boy who ever saw a toad could corroborate, while getting rid of them required the performance of any one of a number of deliciously terrifying rites. Most people who are troubled by common warts have also noted their tendency to spread on persistent contact; for instance, if one has a wart on the inside of one finger, another wart will often develop where the first rubs the adjacent finger. As long ago as 1894, it was shown that warts could be passed from man to man by experimental inoculation and, in 1907, the filtrate from a common wart was shown to cause another similar wart, when injected under the skin of a human volunteer. Warts are tumors, in the precise definition of the term, but they are certainly not cancers nor do they ever become cancerous; that is, they always remain encapsulated and do not invade other tissues or metastasize to other parts of the body. Technically they are known as human papillomas.

Tumorous growths are common in rabbits. In 1931 Richard Shope of The Rockefeller Institute laboratories in Princeton shot a wild cottontail rabbit in New Jersey. Shope was interested in the cancer problem and was delighted to find that on the front and hind feet of this rabbit were small nodules which proved to be fibrous tumors when examined under a microscope. Spontaneous tumors are notoriously temperamental, but every laboratory rabbit which Shope inoculated with cell suspensions of the fibromas developed a tumor at the site of injection. The fibromas grew so rapidly that he knew he was dealing with an infectious agent; the cells themselves just could not have multiplied that vigorously. But, he found, once the virus infection had run its course, the tumors ceased growing and, eventually, nearly all of them regressed.

Also under study at that time at The Rockefeller Institute was another rabbit virus, infectious myxomatosis. In the domestic rabbit and in some wild rabbits, infectious myxomatosis is a rapid fulminating disease; the animals die within a week or two, the mucous membranes of their

respiratory and digestive tracts swollen shut and their
bodies covered with mucus-containing gelatinous tumors.
In the wild South American rabbit, however, the natural
host of the virus, it produces only innocuous nodules
under the skin, very similar to those seen in Shope's rabbits with fibromas. Because of this similarity, Shope tested
the two viruses to see if they were immunologically related; this was about the only method by which relationships between viruses could be studied at that time, before
the days of electron microscopy and practical techniques
for purifying viruses and characterizing them chemically.
He found that rabbits injected with fibroma virus were
resistant to myxomatosis; fibroma, in fact, is now being
used to inoculate domestic rabbits in Australia since the
myxomatosis virus, introduced there about a decade ago,
has made life in Australia almost impossible for the un-
protected rabbit. This perhaps completes the dreary cycle
initiated in 1860 when man first introduced rabbits to
the continent. Shope speculated, "One might . . . suppose that the two viruses were originally identical or at
least had a common ancestor," comparing them to the
viruses of cowpox and smallpox, to which actually, it is
now known, they are related. The fibroma/myxoma viruses are not generally considered tumor viruses. For one
thing, the fibromas are not autonomous, one of the criteria for a tumor. When the virus disappears, the tumor
goes away, just as pox cells cease proliferating when the
active infection has passed. Acute infectious myxomatosis
does not resemble any type of cancer seen in man or
beast; yet if one removed one of the tumorous growths
from these animals, prepared a specimen from it, and gave
it to a pathologist, he would identify it instantly as a
highly malignant sarcoma.

East of the Mississippi, rabbits have fibromas, but the
cottontails west of the Mississippi, especially in Kansas
and Iowa, have a different type of growth. These papillomas, as they are called, sometimes reach six inches in

length, projecting straight out from the animal's body. The outer part of the horny growth is a mass of tough, warty tissue. Shope first heard about the papillomas when he showed his rabbits with fibromas to a visitor from Iowa. The westerner was unimpressed; he had shot rabbits, he said, with horns like Texas steers. Shope bought one of those horns from an Iowa farm boy for a munificent ten dollars and found that these growths, like the fibroma and the myxoma, could be transmitted by a cell-free filtrate, although the papilloma virus does not resemble the fibroma or myxoma agent.

The natural route of infection of these three viruses is not known, but it seems clear that it must be some sort of insect. In the laboratory, the virus can be carried from one animal to another experimentally by the mosquito, but the fact that in wild rabbits the tumors occur most commonly on the footpads seems to indicate that this is not the natural vector. Shope has spent many hours collecting ticks, fleas, chiggers, and other traveling companions of the cottontail without yet identifying the culprit.

Once the papilloma virus had been brought into the laboratory, Shope was interested to see what would happen when it was transmitted to domestic rabbits. He found that these animals also developed papillomas, often ones that grew more vigorously than in the cottontails, but although the cottontail papilloma was usually rich in virus, a cell-free filtrate from the virus-induced papilloma of a domestic rabbit contained no trace of the infective agent and would not produce a tumor in another animal. Yet virus was there. The domestic rabbit's blood contained antibodies against it and indeed, if the papilloma was transplanted and retransplanted from one rabbit to another, even the twelfth rabbit in the series could be shown to have antibodies against the otherwise undetectable virus. If the investigators had not known that the tumors were due to a virus and, furthermore, had not the virus already been identified so antibody tests were possible, there would be no evidence that the domestic rabbit papillomas were of viral origin.

In 1935 Rous and his associate, J. W. Beard, noted the development of cancer in a domestic rabbit with an experimentally induced papilloma. At first the change from papilloma to cancer—from benign to malignant—was thought to occur only in the domestic strain, but soon after, Jerome Syverton of the University of Minnesota noted the progression to cancer in a wild cottontail from Kansas. Subsequently it was found that among animals with papillomas kept for six months or more, twenty-five per cent of the wild rabbits and seventy-five per cent of the domestic rabbits developed cancer in the proliferating tissue at the base of the horny growths. During this latent period, many factors—bacterial infection, slight injury, a number of different chemical carcinogens—could "cause" the cancer. Although the cancerous change would appear at the site of the injury or where the carcinogen had been applied, the tumor was always the same as that induced by the virus alone. Further, although the cancers clearly arose from the virus-induced papillomas, none of the cancers, neither in the domestic rabbit nor in the cottontail, contained detectable virus.

So the first link was forged between a virus and a cancer in mammals. The issue was still confused, however, because although it was clear that in spite of the fact that the virus produced the papilloma, the role of the virus, if any, in the change to carcinoma could not be proven. Arguments such as this, by which the cancer viruses were dismissed for so many years, led Peyton Rous to comment that "the tumor problem is the last stronghold of metaphysics in medicine."

The Milk Agent

Not long after, a third major cancer virus was discovered and this one ended for all time the argument about whether or not viruses produce cancer among the mammalia. Mammary cancers in mice, as in human beings, are one of the most common forms of the disease. Among the early classics of cancer investigations was a series of experiments, running concurrently with Rous's early work on the chicken sarcoma virus, by Leo Loeb in which he showed that breast cancer developed only in the presence of the female hormone. Not long after, Maud Slye, approaching the problem from a totally different direction, showed that by selective inbreeding, strains of mice can be produced in which ninety per cent or more of the animals will develop certain types of cancer while other strains will be virtually cancer-free. The Jackson Memorial Laboratories in Bar Harbor, Maine, grew to be the center for the maintenance and study of these purebred lines, which are still among the most valuable tools of cancer research. In attempts to pin down the nature of the genetic influence on cancer development, crossbreeding experiments were tried between high cancer and low cancer strains, similar to Mendel's crosses between the smooth and wrinkled peas. But mouse mammary cancer refused to follow Mendel's laws. Contrary to all classic genetics, the family background of the mother mouse was obviously far more important than the paternal genealogy.

In 1934 John J. Bittner of the Bar Harbor group began his studies of the mysterious maternal influence. In one experiment he gently removed a whole litter of newborn mice of a high cancer strain from their mother and turned them over for foster nursing to a mouse of a low mammary cancer strain. When the females of the litter matured, far fewer than the expected number developed mammary cancer. Conversely, a litter of low cancer strain mice, wet-nursed by a high cancer strain mother, developed far more than the expected number of breast cancer in later life.

Bittner, who first published his findings in 1936, found

that these mice of high cancer strain contained in their milk a filterable substance which he dubbed, with the characteristic reluctance of cancer investigators to use the word "virus," the mammary cancer milk agent.

There were a number of special features about the mammary cancer milk agent that heavily influenced scientific thought about the relationship between cancer and viruses. First the agent alone would not cause cancer. Bittner maintained from the beginning, and all subsequent work has borne him out, that mammary cancer in the mouse is due to an interplay among at least three factors: hormones, genetics, and the virus. Actually genetics and hormones alone can cause mammary cancer in the absence of virus—or at least in the absence of Bittner's milk virus.

Second, it was found that the mice had to be removed from their mothers immediately after birth, before they had any opportunity to nurse. Even a drop of milk, as little as 0.1 milliliter, from a high cancer strain is sufficient to infect a susceptible newborn mouse. After the first few hours, infection by the viral agent becomes increasingly difficult.

Third, the Bittner virus was found often to coexist with its host for months and even for several generations without making its presence known. During the long latent period—of six to twenty months—between the introduction of the virus and the appearance of cancer in genetically susceptible animals, there are no signs of disease, although virus can be isolated from the milk, and so passed on to newborns, and from tissues of the high cancer strains. An animal of low cancer strain can carry the virus all its life without ever showing signs of cancer. Male mice of high cancer strains, although they never develop mammary cancer unless they are given female hormones, can pass the virus to females at mating; this is apparently the only other natural route of spread of the virus, since contact infection does not seem to occur.

Fourth, as a result of Bittner's discovery, the cancer-inducing viruses could no longer be ignored or dismissed as exceptions that proved the "rules" of expected cancer or virus behavior. A virus had been shown to be responsible for the most common form of cancer in the most commonly used laboratory animals and, from that time onward, viruses, although still unwelcome, were in the cancer picture to stay.

4 The Friendly Viruses

From time to time, nature, properly regarded as purpose-less, blind, and hence without mischief, compassion, or humor, seems to become aware of man's groping attempts to probe her complexities and, like a fond but impatient mother, presses the right implement into his hand. So, just at the critical moment, she gave Drosophila to the ge-neticist, the giant axon of the squid to the neurophysiolo-gists, and to the virologist, surely the most precious of her treasures, the bacteriophage.

The recipient of this gift was Max Delbrück. Delbrück was a physicist trained in Germany who came to the United States in 1937. Because of his nationality, he was not able to engage in "sensitive" scientific work, nor, as he has made clear, was he inclined to. As a consequence, Delbrück and the brilliant group that collected about him during the war years laid the foundations not just for modern research in basic virology but also for the new molecular genetics, which now has grown to dominate completely all of the life sciences, as it will for years to come.

Actually, as often happens, the bacteriophages, or bac-terial viruses, had been waiting for a Delbrück for some twenty years. They were first discovered in 1915 by F. W. Twort, a London bacteriologist. Twort was growing bac-teria on agar, a jelly-like broth on which bacterial cells spread out to form a luxurious lawn. From time to time, however, Twort noted bare or, as he called them, "glassy" patches on his cultures. If he touched a glass rod to one of these patches and then touched it to another point on the bacterial colony, a new glassy patch appeared. Filtering the fluid did not change its ability to make bacteria disappear.

In 1917 the bacteriophages were rediscovered by Felix d'Hérelle of the Pasteur Institute in Paris, a man of passionate conviction. He isolated them from the intestinal tract of a boy suffering from dysentery, observed their effects on the causative bacteria, and, from that moment forward, believed that bacterial viruses could be used to wipe bacterial disease from the face of the earth. "The history of an epidemic," d'Hérelle proclaimed, "is, in the last analysis, the story of an infection with two microorganisms. The epidemic ceases at the moment when all susceptible individuals harbor a bacteriophage active for the causative organism of the epidemic."

In support of this contention, d'Hérelle filled notebooks with observations correlating the presence of phage with the recovery from disease in scores of patients with dysentery. He gave patients suspensions of bacteriophage and watched their clinical progress. Fired by his enthusiasm, public health workers throughout India and Asia seeded the public drinking water with bacterial viruses, not once but again and again, in attempts to hold back epidemics of cholera, dysentery, and the plague.

The results were disappointing. In retrospect, it is easy to understand why. It is true, as d'Hérelle established, that almost every known type of bacteria is susceptible to one and often to many different "bacteria eaters," but a slight mutation on either side destroys this intimate relationship. Also, although phage has no difficulty making its way from cell to cell in a closely packed laboratory culture, it is more difficult to maintain a chain reaction of infection in the disorderly environment of the intestinal tract.

Many of d'Hérelle's observations on the nature of the bacterial viruses were astonishingly astute and accurate, considering the crudeness of the techniques then available for his work. He maintained phages must be particulate in nature, pointing out that if one greatly diluted the filtrate and then spread a microdrop of it over a large bacterial colony, one did not get an over-all, weak effect, but rather discrete foci of activity which would be separated further and further apart, depending on the degree of dilution of the microdrop. He also correctly described the infectious cycle of this hypothetical invisible particle: attachment to the bacterial cell, penetration of the cell, a latent period of some twenty to forty minutes, bursting, or lysis, of the infected bacterium, and release of 100 to 200 new "young corpuscles."

D'Hérelle was the sort who attracted opponents, of whom Jules Bordet, Belgian physiologist and Nobel laureate, was the most vocal. Bordet held that phages were a "microbian transmissible autolysis," produced by bacteria. They were not in any sense "living," but an enzymatic product excreted by a sick cell, which, when it came in contact with other cells, caused them, in turn, to secrete more of the noxious enzyme. This opinion, with some slight variations, was held by many distinguished scientists until late in the 1930s.

The question of whether or not bacteriophages were simply a product of bacterial metabolism was aggravated by a phenomenon that came to be known as lysogeny, which actually was the basis of Twort's original observation. If two strains of bacteria are growing together in a common culture, from time to time phages will suddenly appear in the colony, completely wiping out one of the strains. This occurs even though the cultures are rigorously protected from outside invaders. D'Hérelle interpreted the relationship between phage and bacterium as an example of symbiosis. Bordet, who had a flair for rhetoric, proclaimed that "the power of reproducing the bacteriophage is woven into the hereditary web of the bacterium." Several decades passed before it could be shown that both were right.

D'Hérelle, more than anyone else, kept the controversy alive. He was clearly a gifted scientist, but he was never able to modify his initial concepts of the bacteriophage, and they constricted him like a vise. Under fire, he became such an ardent champion of the unique properties of the phage, that he refused to let them be associated, even taxonomically, with other common infectious agents. Not only were the bacteriophages unrelated to viruses—animal, plant, or insect—he maintained, but also unrelated to what he somewhat deprecatingly referred to as the "Twort phenomenon."

Although d'Hérelle's chief interest in the bacterial viruses was as a panacea for bacterial ills, he too, like Beijerinck, glimpsed that they held some special mystery, giving them the name of *Protobios* to emphasize their position in the hierarchy of the animate. "The fact that the bacteriophage corpuscle has been demonstrated to be a simple protein micella, and that it is a living being, shows that the cellular concept of life is erroneous," d'Hérelle wrote. Not long after, in 1933, a young German biochemist, Max Schlesinger, reported that bacteriophages were composed half of protein and half of deoxyribonucleic acid, but this report came so long before its time that it was largely overlooked.

By the end of the 1930s, the controversy faded, its contentions outmoded and its protagonists old and weary. The sulfa drugs had been discovered and the last therapeutic assays with phage were being slowly abandoned. The bacteriophages came to be included among the other "filterable viruses," tentatively at first and then, largely because most virologists thought the matter academic and unimportant, with greater and greater assurance. D'Hérelle did not die until 1949 but by this time the bacteriophages had escaped to lead a life of their own. Ironically, for d'Hérelle was a brilliant man, it seems that he never followed the work of Delbrück and his "school" or recognized its importance.

Delbrück, "taking sides neither with the viruses nor with the bacteria," as he put it, saw in this simple system an unusual opportunity for studying how living things replicate, one of the central problems of all biology. Phage were inexpensive, readily available, and demanded little space or equipment, essential factors for any program not part of the war effort. Further, phages were phenomenal at reproducing themselves; hundreds of progeny appeared within minutes. Since every experiment took only a few hours, Delbrück calculated (as he recalled ruefully some years later) that the entire problem could not possibly take long to solve.

Others were quick to see the possibilities, first Salvador Luria, Alfred Hershey, T. F. Anderson and A. H. Doermann some of whom, like Delbrück, were aliens—and soon enemy aliens—and so excluded from the mainstream of scientific effort. Around this nucleus condensed one of the most extraordinary groups in all of biological history —a group which developed not only a new field of research, both its basic concepts and its methodology, but also a tradition of co-operation, mutual respect, excitement, and critical curiosity that has now passed undiminished through three intellectual generations of bacteriophage investigators and has pervaded far beyond these boundaries. Others soon joined, chief among them Seymour Cohen and Mark Adams. They were of different disciplines, different nationalities, different personalities, from different institutions; there was no trace of formal organization, and probably no formal organization could ever have bound these highly individualistic investigators together. Delbrück himself was a strong unifying influence; he had worked under Niels Bohr in the early 1930s and brought with him, as part of his scientific baggage, "the spirit of Copenhagen," the generous pooling of interests and free exchange of ideas that had done so much to advance the early work on the structure of the atom. In this instance, too, as in this early time in Europe, they knew the subject was an important one. "A strong feeling of adventure is animating those who are working on the bacterial viruses," said Delbrück early in these investigations, "a feeling that they have a small part in the great drive toward a fundamental problem in biology."

Right at the beginning, the bacteriophage researchers were touched by good fortune. About the time the group began to form, the first viruses were seen by the electron microscope. The maximum practical range of magnification with a light microscope is about 2000 times. This brings the largest viruses, such as smallpox, just over the threshold of visibility. The electron microscope, with the much shorter wave length of its beam, can produce much finer resolutions, bringing even the smallest viruses well within its range. When the leap was first made, however, from the light to the electron microscope, it was very hard to know what one was seeing, particularly since the methods of preparation for electron microscopy may produce changes in the material being studied. In those early days, many of the animal viruses showed up as blobs or drops, not clearly distinguishable from the other varied and unclassified contents of the cells in which they were found. In 1941 Helmut Ruska, the brother of the chief developer of electron microscopy, reported having examined material prepared from infected bacteria and having seen in it strange club-shaped objects. In the following year, Luria and Delbrück and Anderson purified phages, took electron micrographs of the purified preparation, and found that they did indeed have tails, as Ruska's work had indicated. In fact, they looked remarkably like tadpoles. (See Plate 3.) The discovery that they had such a definite and highly characteristic shape was not only a help in identifying them, but also the fact that anything so small—some 1,000,000,000 of them could be laid out inside a single letter "o" on this page—could be so complexly fashioned increased the investigators' respect, delight, and curiosity. Even today, when the now very familiar figure of the tadpole-shaped bacteriophage is flashed on the screen at a scientific meeting, as it often is, a sense of pleasure passes through the audience, similar to that felt on viewing a photograph of a beloved child.

From the beginning, the question was where the new viruses come from. To simplify the problem to some extent, the group, by common consent, concentrated on a small number of phages, a group of seven which had in common the ability to infect one particular strain of bacteria, *Escherichia coli*, a common and harmless inhabitant of the human digestive tract. By that time a convention had been established of giving letter-number combinations to phage by which they could be identified, like civil service employees or members of the British Secret Service, and these seven strains came to be called T1 through T7. Those with even numbers, the T-even phage, had thicker, stubbier tails than the T-odd phage, and all could be distinguished from one another immunologically and also by slight differences in their biological activity. As it has turned out, almost all of the major work has been done with T2 and T4.

First, they tried to find the phage inside the cell during the so-called latent period, between the moment the original virus disappeared within the cell and the time at which new particles appeared. Ways had not yet been perfected for slicing cells into thin sections, and the electron microscope was not able to peer into the dark whale-like interior of *E. coli*, so Doermann worked out methods by which cells could be lysed or broken open at different stages during the latent period without their contents being destroyed. He found that if the cell membranes were artificially ruptured any time during the first half of the latent period (which came to be known as the eclipse), no infective particles could be recovered and the microscope's X-ray eye could not find a single particle—not even the one that had initiated the infection—in the spilled-out contents of the cell. During the second half of the latent period, depending on when the cell was opened, increasing numbers of completed phage could be found and, mixed with them, spherical particles that resembled phage heads. The phage increased at a regular rate during this time, not geometrically—2, 4, 8, 16, 32, 64, like bacteria—but linearly, one after another, as if they were coming off an assembly line.

Experiments were made in which one E. coli was infected with several phage particles. Up to ten might infect a single cell, but there would be no increase in the total number of particles produced nor any decrease in the latent period. If a bacterial cell was infected simultaneously with two types of phage, such as T2 and T4, both types might be released simultaneously, although there would be no increase in the total yield.

Hershey, working at the Carnegie Institute's genetics research unit, noticed that modifications would appear from time to time in viruses, just as mutants appeared from time to time in bacterial strains. A substrain of T2 would suddenly develop, for instance, that would infect another strain of E. coli that the parent T2 could not infect. This substrain T2h (h for host range) would then breed true, producing countless T2h progeny. Other mutants were found, T2r and T4r (with r standing for rapid), that lysed the bacterial cell more quickly than did the parent phage.

Delbrück and Hershey, working in their separate laboratories but in constant communication, found at just about the same time, in 1946, that if E. coli B was infected simultaneously with T4r and T2, for example, one would get T4 and T2r as well as T4r and T2. Similarly, infection with T2h and T2r would yield T2h, T2r, T2, and T2hr. Bacteriophages were engaged in something very much like mating, producing new phages that were crosses between the parent strains. At this instant, virology and genetics met.

Not long after, Luria found that if he irradiated bacteriophages with ultraviolet light, they could still infect, but no phage progeny would be produced by any single particle. If, however, there was an excess of bacteriophages, so that each cell was infected with several particles, live progeny would appear. Apparently several damaged phages could get together to form a whole one. One could explain both of these phenomena, the mating and the "recovery" after irradiation, by assuming that the bacteriophages had chromosomes, meaning simply some structure on which their genetic characteristics were arranged. These chromosomes would get together in the bacterial cell and exchange characteristics. In this way, new chromosomes could be formed that combined some features of each of the original ones, and a damaged chromosome could be repaired by a patch from another that might be damaged, too, but in a different way.

Some thirty years before, in T. H. Morgan's laboratory at Columbia, it had been shown in the fruit fly that such crossing over and recombination occurred during the formation of the egg and sperm cells. In the bacteriophage, as in the fruit fly, it now began to be possible to make a chromosomal map, depending on the frequencies with which new combinations appeared. For example, as Figure 2 shows, two genetic characteristics located very far apart on the chromosome would have a very high frequency of recombination, whereas two very close together could rarely be separated from one another by chance chromosomal breaks. Mapping the chromosome of the bacteriophage did not become highly developed for another decade, but the foundations for this work, as for many other aspects of bacteriophage research, were laid during the 1940s.

By 1949 a number of other workers had confirmed Schlesinger's early studies showing that bacteriophages were composed in almost equal quantities of protein and deoxyribonucleic acid (almost ready to assume the now

(A)

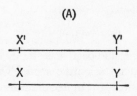

(B)   (C)

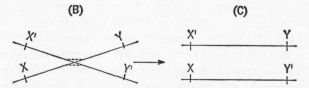

Figure 2. When the chromosomes break and recombine, genetic characteristics, such as X and Y', which once appeared on separate chromosomes, may now be present on the same chromosome. The frequency with which such recombinations occur depends on the distance between the marker genes. (After Weidel.)

familiar abbreviation of DNA). At this point, Anderson discovered that if phage particles were suspended in a high concentration of ordinary salt, and then the solution was diluted very rapidly—in effect plunging them from one medium to another—the phages were inactivated; this did not occur if the concentration of salt in the medium was changed slowly. Under the electron microscope the inactivated phages looked like tadpole-shaped ghosts, their heads hollow and empty. When these empty heads were studied chemically, it was found that they consisted only of protein. The DNA had leaked out. Apparently, in the intact phage, the DNA was inside the protein head. The sudden change in pressure going from one salt concentration to another ruptured this head, the DNA leaked out, and the particle was then inactive. This was the first really major clue as to how phages were put together and how they worked.

Radioactive Tracers

About this time, radioactive isotopes began to become available for general scientific work. These isotopes are chemically identical to more ordinary atomic forms—iodine 131 looks and tastes the same as ordinary iodine, for instance, and carbon 14 will serve the same chemical, and, therefore, biological functions as the common carbon atom—and so they will readily take their place in any reactions of living organisms. Because they are physically unstable, these particles emit energy which can be detected by a Geiger counter or by photographic film, and so they can be used as tags or labels to identify and follow various chemical substances in living systems. Cohen was the first to use these to answer some of the questions posed by the bacteriophage. He wanted to know where the DNA and protein of the phage came from. DNA contained phosphorus, but no sulfur, and protein contained sulfur, but no phosphorus; therefore, by using radioactive sulfur and radioactive phosphorus, two common isotopes, it would be possible to label either one of the components and not the other. Cohen added radioactive sulfur and radioactive phosphorus to a culture in which bacteria were growing and simultaneously infected the culture with bacteriophages. When the new progeny of the phage were produced, they were found to be tagged with radioactive labels. This answered an important question: phages were not hidden in the cell before infection, waiting to be released by the trigger of the infecting particle, as d'Hérelle's adversaries had contended. They were synthesized in the cell after infection, using raw material present in the medium. This experiment also provided an important tool, bacteriophage with the DNA carrying one tag and the protein another.

Hershey, in what is certainly the most famous single experiment ever performed in the history of bacteriophage research, and perhaps in all of modern virology, prepared labeled T2 in this fashion and used them to infect a fresh culture of bacteria. When freshly infected bacteria were analyzed, all of the radioactive phosphorus was found inside the cell and almost all of the radioactive sulfur was found outside of it. Electron micrographs confirmed that

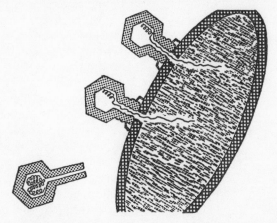

Figure 3. The bacteriophage attaches itself to the bacterial cell wall and injects its DNA into the cell, leaving its empty protein coat outside. (After drawing in *Sloan-Kettering Institute Progress Report* XV, 1963.)

the empty phage heads were left outside the cell; these could be sheared off the cell wall and infection would still proceed. In other words, the protein was just a container. It was the DNA that entered the cell, the DNA that set up the infectious cycle and caused the production of more DNA and more protein, and that carried, all alone, the hereditary message of the bacteriophage particle. Now, virology, genetics, and biochemistry flowed together to form the rushing current of modern biological research.

Part II

THE NEW GENETICS

5   The Slender Thread

From this point onward, virology and cellular genetics became so intertwined that it is necessary to stop a moment to look at some events that had taken place in what appeared, before Hershey's experiment, to be other corners of the scientific world.

Few chemistry textbooks written before 1950 had much to say about DNA, although it was first discovered in 1868, now virtually a century ago. Friedrich Miescher, working at that time in the famous laboratories of Hoppe-Seyler in Tübingen, was interested in studying the chemical composition of cell nuclei. He collected human white cells, pus, from surgical bandages, exposed them to pepsin to dissolve the proteins and cellular debris, and discovered that he had left a white sugary substance, very slightly acid, which contained phosphorus. Miescher's name for it, nucleic acid, was later amended to deoxyribonucleic acid to distinguish it from a closely related chemical, ribonucleic acid, which subsequently was also isolated from the cell.

In 1914 the German chemist Robert Fuelgen discovered that DNA had a remarkable attraction for fuscin dye, but considered this finding so unimportant that he did not trouble to report it for a decade. Fuelgen staining, as it was called when it finally made its way into use, revealed that DNA was characteristically located in the nucleus and that it was contained in all living cells.

In 1928 an experiment was performed which seemed at that time very remote from either biochemistry, genetics, or certainly virology. Frederick Griffith, a public health bacteriologist, was studying the bacillus that causes pneumonia, then the grim "captain of the men of death." Pneumococci come in either virulent (disease-causing) or avirulent (harmless) forms. The virulent pneumococci are easily distinguishable under the microscope because they are surrounded by protective capsules and form colonies which are smooth in appearance. Several different strains of pneumococci are known, each of which has capsules that are slightly different chemically and thus distinct immunologically from those of the other strains. The avirulent pneumococci are without capsules and so their colonies appear rough.

Griffith was interested in finding out whether injections of heat-killed virulent pneumococci, which do not cause disease, might be used to vaccinate against pneumonia. In the course of his work, he injected mice simultaneously with heat-killed virulent bacteria and with unencapsulated living bacteria. Since each of these were known to be harmless, Griffith was surprised to find that all of the mice died and that on autopsy all of their bodies yielded living pneumococci with capsules.

The results of a subsequent experiment were even more puzzling. Type II pneumococci with no capsules were injected into mice simultaneously with Type I pneumococci that were encapsulated but had been killed. Again the mice died and live pneumococci could be recovered, the recovered organisms wearing capsules—but apparently the wrong capsules. All of the live bacteria had been Type II, but all of the capsules, as determined immunologically, were of Type I. Moreover, these bacteria as they divided transmitted to their progeny, generation after generation, the ability to make Type I capsules.

Because of the seriousness of pneumonia as a medical problem, Griffith's experiment attracted a great deal of attention. Within the next few years, it was shown that this same phenomenon could be reproduced in the test tube and, finally, that extracts from the killed, smooth bacteria, if added to the living, rough bacteria in the test tube, could transmit to the living cells—and through them to their progeny—the ability to make capsules. In other words, the cells somehow—it was a biological heresy —acquired an hereditary characteristic.

One of the laboratories that worked on the nature of the transforming factor, as it came to be called, was that of O. T. Avery at The Rockefeller Institute. After almost a decade, Avery and his coworkers, Colin MacLoed and Maclyn McCarty, were able to dissect out and identify the substance from the killed bacteria that transmitted the new genetic quality. It was, totally unexpectedly, the DNA. These isolated molecules were the substance of heredity.

The "Inborn Errors"

Other investigators, in the meantime, had been seeking to define exactly what was meant by an hereditary characteristic. In England, in 1908, Sir Archibald Garrod described a group of human diseases which he termed "the inborn errors of metabolism." With a leap of the imagination that spanned half a century, Garrod postulated that certain human ills were caused by the lack of a specific enzyme and, further, that the absence of the normal enzyme reflected the absence of the normal form of a specific gene.

In the early 1940s, geneticist George W. Beadle and biologist Edward L. Tatum laid the experimental foundations under Garrod's brilliant guess. Genetics until that time had been concerned largely with superficial characteristics, blue versus yellow eyes or six toes as compared to five. It is obvious if you think about it that a child inherits from its parents not only a vague physical resemblance but also every single one of the vital functions that enable it to exist as an organism, whether it is a human being, a fruit fly, or a wrinkled pea. Yet there did not seem to be any way to study these vital functions since, by definition, if one of them was lacking, the organism could not survive.

To confront this problem, Beadle and Tatum found the red bread mold *Neurospora crassa*. *Neurospora* offered two big advantages for their study. First, like many simple organisms, it was haploid, which means simply that it has only one copy of its genetic information, instead of two like human beings have, so a mutation could not be masked or compensated for as it may in man. Second, *Neurospora* was extremely self-sufficient. Man can make only half of the twenty biologically important amino acids. "Normal" *Neurospora* can make every one of them. To grow, it needs only a very simple medium containing a few organic compounds such as phosphate, nitrate, and sulfate, and one of the B vitamins.

Beadle and Tatum prepared a whole series of media— both simple media and enriched media containing various assortments of amino acids. Then they exposed samples of the mold to radiation to increase its mutation rate. When they tested the ability of the irradiated mold to grow in the various types of media, they found, as they had anticipated, that the mutations, in some cases, made the mold unable to make a particular amino acid; it could survive only in suitably enriched media. Amino acids, in molds and in men, are made in a series of biosynthetic steps, each governed by a very specific enzyme. When the mutant molds were analyzed, it was found that in each case the loss of function could be traced to the loss of one particular enzyme. "One gene—one enzyme," Beadle and Tatum concluded, or, more precisely, as it came to be stated, one gene—one protein.

The Structure of Proteins

The proteins of most living things are made up of combinations of up to twenty different kinds of amino acids

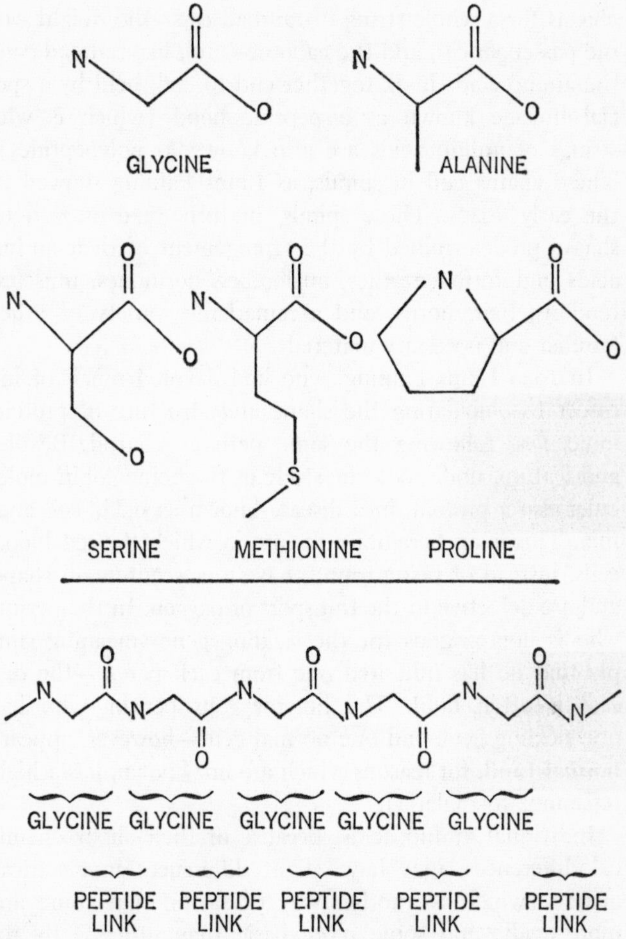

Figure 4. Proteins are chains of amino acids, all of which contain the same basic structure or "backbone" and which are joined together by peptide links to form the long chains characteristic of protein molecules.

linked together in long chains. All amino acids have the same basic structure on which is superimposed a variety of other atomic groups, just as one might use the same chassis for a whole string of railroad cars—the freight car, the passenger car, and the caboose—and, like railroad cars, the amino acids hook together end to end, held by a special linkage known as a peptide bond (which is why strings of amino acids are also known as polypeptides). These chains coil in spirals, as Linus Pauling showed in the early 1940s. These spirals, in turn, take on various shapes predetermined by the arrangement of their amino acids and form enzymes, antibodies, hormones, muscles, tendons, hair, horns, and a remarkable variety of other familiar and necessary materials.

In 1949 Linus Pauling, who had devoted much of his career to elucidating the shape and structure of protein molecules, following the same path as Garrod, Beadle, and Tatum, undertook the study of the hemoglobin molecule, also a protein, in a disease known as sickle cell anemia. This is an hereditary disease in which the red blood cells, instead of being round, have a crescent-moon shape and are defective in the transport of oxygen. In the person who is homozygous for the sickling gene—meaning simply that he has inherited one from each parent—the disease is often fatal. The heterozygous person—who has one sickling gene and one normal gene—however, appears normal (and, for reasons which are not known, has a high resistance to malaria).

Individual amino acids, because of their slight chemical differences, may have slight differences in electrical charge (which is another way of saying that some are more acidic and some more basic than others). By recording the behavior of the molecules in an electric field, Pauling was able to show that the hemoglobin of sickle cell anemia is just a little different from normal hemoglobin. Furthermore, the person heterozygous for sickle cell anemia produces two hemoglobins, both the normal one and the abnormal one. As Pauling put it, this was a molecular disease. Subsequently Vernon Ingram of Cambridge was able to show that the difference between the two hemoglobins was one amino acid in a chain of 300.

The Role of DNA

Biochemists were slow to accept the idea that DNA was the stuff of heredity. Pauling and others thought, for example, that the gene was composed of protein molecules which served as the templates for the working proteins in the cytoplasm. However, within the decade after Avery's demonstration that DNA was the transforming principle in pneumococcus, there were three additional experimental proofs that this deceptively simple chemical did indeed carry the genetic determinants. All of these experiments, as it turned out, also had important effects on the subsequent growth of understanding about the nature of the viruses.

The first of these was reported in 1946 by Joshua Lederberg and Edward Tatum, then at Yale. They mixed together two strains of *E. coli* K 12, a close relative of the bacterial cells that are hosts to the T-even phage. The strains could be distinguished because one of them could not make two amino acids that could be made by the second strain, and the second strain could not make two amino acids that could be made by the first. When the two were permitted to grow together in a medium containing all four amino acids plus all the other requirements, a peculiar event took place which in most laboratories would have been overlooked. From time to time, an *E. coli* K 12 cell appeared that could make all four amino acids, and it and its offspring could grow in a medium that supplied none of them.

When Lederberg and Tatum studied their mixed colony microscopically, they finally discovered that bacteria, long thought constrained to the joyless process of cell division, were mating. From time to time two cells would conjugate; one would send out a narrow cytoplasmic bridge to

the other and across this bridge would send genetic information. So a cell which could make only two of the
missing amino acids could be given the ability to make
the other two and, most important, could transmit these
useful new functions to a whole new colony of bacteria.
And the substance that was transferred from one bacterial
cell to another, it was subsequently found, was simply
DNA. Beadle, Lederberg, and Tatum shared the Nobel
Prize in physiology and medicine for their studies in
Neurospora and this closely related work on bacterial
conjugation.

François Jacob and Elie Wollman of the Pasteur Institute became interested in conjugation as a tool for studying bacterial genetics. For this purpose, they selected
strains that differed in a number of characteristics, so
they would have a series of measurable traits, genetic
markers, to follow. Conjugation takes about an hour.
They found that if they shook the cells apart while they
were conjugating (it is done in a Waring blender), they
were not damaged and that the recipient cell, when analyzed for genetic markers, contained only a few but not
all of the markers. By repeating the experiment over and
over and separating different couples at different times,
they were able to show that new traits are introduced
into the cell one at a time, the first by the end of six minutes, the second at eight minutes, and so on, each one
following the other with its assigned cargo. In other
words, this experiment showed that the genes were strung
along the chromosome just like beads along a string, as
the older geneticists had envisioned them. But both beads
and string were DNA.

Not long after, Norton Zinder, working with Lederberg at the University of Wisconsin, when Zinder was
still a graduate student, attempted to repeat the experiment of Lederberg and Tatum using strains of another
bacterium, *Salmonella*, rather than *E. coli*. When they
mixed the two colonies together, an exchange of genetic

characteristics did take place, but no orderly array of markers entered the recipient cells, just one here and one there and, at most and very occasionally, two together. One strain was doing all the giving and another all the receiving and, besides, no cells could be found conjugating.

Convinced that something besides mating was taking place, Zinder and Lederberg separated the two colonies by a filter too fine to let any of the cells slip through and again, with the same frequency, one cell acquired the genetic traits of another. Working from this clue, they examined the fluid bathing the colonies and discovered that it was full of viruses. One of the bacterial strains, they discovered, was lysogenic; that is, it harbored bacteriophages which usually remained quiescent and temperate within the cell. From time to time, one of the phages would terminate its friendly symbiotic relationship with the cell and set out to make new particles, destroying its erstwhile host as it did so. The new particles, in the process of packaging their own genetic equipment in the new protein receptacles, picked up, like visitors leaving a summer hotel, some souvenirs of their stay, scraps of the genetic equipment of the bacterium they were vacating. These they would carry with them to the new host cell and, when they settled down again into lysogeny, the imported genes would become by transduction part of the new cell's standard equipment. And, as with T_2 bacteriophage, only DNA—the DNA of the phage and the DNA of the bacterium—entered the new host cell. When Hershey's experiment made it clear that DNA and DNA alone was injected into the new host cell by the bacteriophage, it also became evident that the transduced bacterial gene could be no more than one discrete fragment of DNA.

The third of these experiments was that of Hershey, described at the end of the last chapter, which simultaneously affirmed the role of DNA in a second biological system, the virus, and also set modern virology on its present course.

These four brilliant experimental proofs—transformation, conjugation, transduction, and viral infection—established conclusively the role of DNA as the bearer of heredity.

The Structure of DNA

By the time of Avery's discovery, DNA was known to consist of a rather simple group of constituents: a kind of sugar, phosphate, and four fairly unusual chemicals known as the nitrogenous bases. These nitrogenous bases were adenine and guanine (which belong to a class known as purines) and thymine and cytosine (which are pyrimidines). The chief authority on nucleic acid structure at that time was P. A. Levene, also of The Rockefeller Institute. Levene broke down DNA and showed that each of the nitrogenous bases was always attached to a molecule of sugar and a molecule of phosphate; this more complex group was called a nucleotide. He then postulated that the four possible nucleotides always cluster together to form a tetranucleotide and that in nature all DNA was formed of steadily repeating tetranucleotide units. This hypothesis of Levene's dominated the scientific field for more than a decade and was the anvil against which the present concepts of DNA were beaten out.

The problem was, of course, that the idea of DNA as a regularly repeating, monotonous structure was completely at odds with the work in viruses and bacteria that indicated that the DNA molecule must carry a great variety of very complicated biological messages. In fact, it was for this reason that most biologists were convinced that protein with its twenty amino acids, so persuasively close to our own twenty-six-letter alphabet, must carry the "message of life." This idea was so overpowering that it was not until years after Avery's very explicit findings

that DNA came to be generally recognized as the bearer
of the hereditary information.

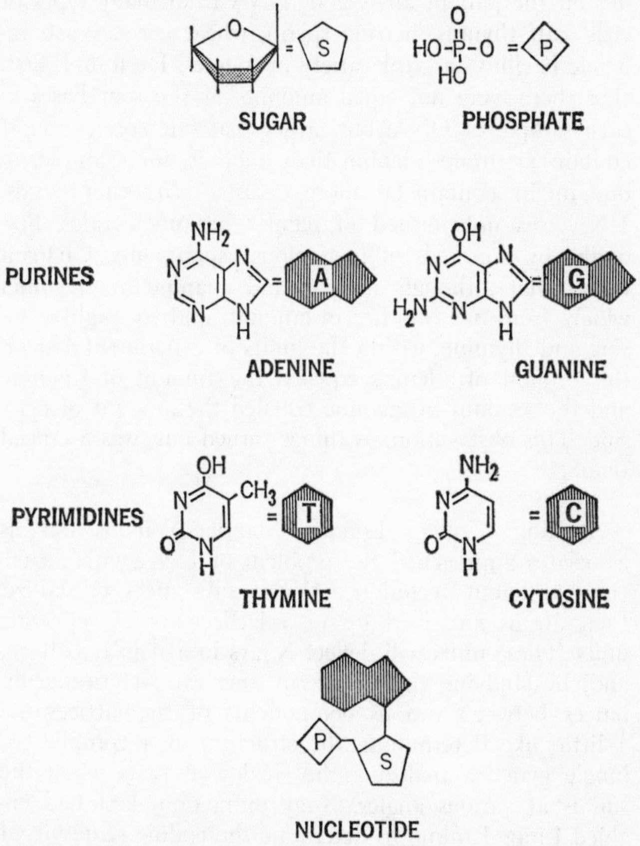

SUGAR   PHOSPHATE

PURINES

ADENINE   GUANINE

PYRIMIDINES

THYMINE   CYTOSINE

NUCLEOTIDE

Figure 5. The nucleotides, the building blocks of DNA, are composed of three different types of submolecule. One of these is the
sugar, shown on the upper left, and the second is the phosphate
group shown on the upper right. In addition, each nucleotide contains one of four possible nitrogenous bases, either adenine or guanine (the purines) or thymine or cytosine (the pyrimidines). The
diagram at the bottom shows schematically the way in which a
purine, a sugar, and a phosphate group join together to form a
nucleotide. (After a drawing in a *Sloan-Kettering Institute Progress
Report.*)

One of those troubled by the Avery-Levene paradox was Erwin Chargaff of Columbia University. Chargaff set out on the patient analysis of DNA from many types of cells, calf thymus, herring sperm, wheat germ, yeast, tubercle bacillus—a great variety of sources. He found, first, that there were not equal amounts of the four bases in each sample of DNA, but rather that one species might contain far more adenine than another, for example, or one might contain far more cytosine. In other words, DNA was not formed of regular tetranucleotides. Secondly, by hundreds of meticulous experiments, Chargaff found that although adenine and guanine might differ widely from one another in amount, and so might cytosine and thymine, within the limits of experimental error, the amount of adenine equaled the amount of thymine and the amount of guanine equaled the amount of cytosine. This observation, as things turned out, was a crucial one.

At King's College, London, Maurice Wilkins and his associates approached the problem of DNA with an entirely different technique. When substances crystallize, their atoms are lined up in a latticework of repeating units. These units will deflect X-rays in a regular pattern, and, by studying these patterns, one can determine distances between various components of the latticework, a little like determining the structure of a complicated jungle gym by analyzing the shadow it casts when the sun is at various angles. X-ray diffraction data had enabled Linus Pauling to determine the coiling structure of protein molecules, and now Wilkins was making them available for similar studies on DNA.

In 1951 James Watson, who had studied with Luria at the Massachusetts Institute of Technology, went to Cambridge, England, on a research fellowship to learn about molecular structure. There, at the Cavendish Laboratory, he met physicist Francis Crick. Both were intensely interested in the riddle of the structure of DNA and immediately set about the work that was to solve it. Watson and Crick did no experiments in the usual sense. They worked entirely with other people's material, the findings of Levene, the data of Chargaff, the X-ray pictures of Wilkins. They were very conscious of the biological role of DNA. In order to carry such a vast amount of information, the molecules should be heterogeneous and varied. Also, although they were not addressing this problem directly, they knew that there must be some way for them to replicate readily and with a most fantastic precision in order that faithful copies could be passed from cell to cell, from parent to offspring, through eons and eons. But, of course, these ideas had never been put to such a rigorous test before; maybe chemical structure did not necessarily reflect function. Perhaps there was no direct relationship at all. "In pessimistic moods," Watson recalls, "we often worried that the correct structure might be dull—that is, that it would suggest absolutely nothing."

It turned out, in fact, to be "unbelievably interesting." Wilkins' data seemed to indicate that the DNA molecule was a double helix, like a spiral staircase with two bannisters, or railings, one winding up and one winding down. These railings, which composed the rigid backbones of the double helix, were made up of sugar and phosphate molecules, alternating. Perpendicular to the railings, like the steps in the staircase or the rungs in a twisted ladder, were the nitrogenous bases, one base for each sugar-phosphate, as Levene had shown. The bases that were perpendicular to the two opposing sugar-phosphate chains met across the helix and were joined together by hydrogen bonds, the relatively weak, omnipresent chemical bonds that Pauling had demonstrated in his studies of the structure of proteins. The distance across the helix, according to Wilkins' measurements, was twenty Angstroms (an Angstrom is equal to one-hundred-millionth of a centimeter). Two purines in combination would take up more than twenty Angstroms, and two pyrimidines would not reach all the way across. But if a purine paired, in each case, with a pyrimidine, there would be an exact fit, and, indeed, this is the way it is.

Then Watson and Crick considered Chargaff's data

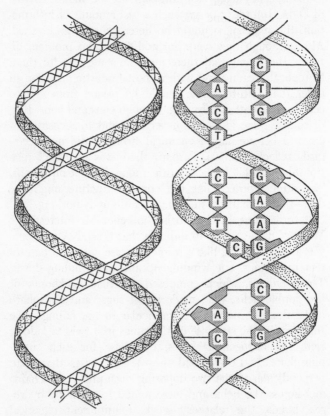

Figure 6. The structure of DNA, as deduced by Watson and Crick, is a double helix or a twisted ladder. The sugars and phosphates of the nucleotides form the sides of the ladder, and attached to each sugar-phosphate, at a right angle, is a nitrogenous base. Combinations of two bases, one from each side, form the rungs of the ladder. Of great biological importance is the fact that adenine can pair only with thymine, or vice versa, to make such a rung and guanine only with cytosine. (After *Sloan-Kettering Progress Report*.)

and got the most felicitous notion of all. Suppose adenine always had to pair with thymine and suppose guanine always had to pair with cytosine. This would satisfy all the physicochemical requirements and conform to Chargaff's measurements, which said that thymine had to equal adenine, and guanine had to equal cytosine. It would provide for all the hoped-for heterogeneity, since along any one strand, any arrangement of bases was possible. But it would do much more. One strand of DNA would always be complementary to the other. Whenever there was an adenine on the first strand, there would have to be a thymine on the second, and the same with guanine and cytosine. Suddenly a beautiful and simple means for the replication of DNA emerged from the mathematical data. Suppose at replication the two strands separated, opening up along the hydrogen bonds. Then suppose each strand served as a template along which its complement could be formed; this new partner would have to resemble the previous partner exactly, and the two new double helices would then be exact copies of the first. Within a few years Mathew Meselson of the California Institute of Technology showed with isotopes that in bacteria newly formed DNA is, as predicted, made up of one old strand and one new strand. About the same time, Arthur Kornberg of Stanford isolated the enzyme that, when given a single strand of DNA and all the necessary nucleotides, will assemble them into a new double-helixed molecule, with the new strand the exact complement of the old.

So, in one incredibly rapid chain of events, the process underlying self-replication—one of the primary attributes of all organisms—was suddenly revealed. And those who at the moment when Watson and Crick made their historic announcement, in 1953, could think of no better phrase than "the secret of life" were on this occasion almost justified.

6   The Making of Proteins

In 1937, two years after Stanley first crystallized tobacco mosaic virus, the British biochemists Frederick Bawden and Norman Pirie discovered that the virus was not a pure protein, as Stanley had thought. A small amount, five per cent by weight, of the molecule consisted of ribonucleic acid, or, as it came to be known in the subsequent course of events, RNA. Like DNA, RNA had been studied very little at that time. It was first isolated about the turn of the century, and since it was originally found in plant cells, it was believed for some time that RNA was the plant's equivalent of DNA, an issue not very hotly argued since neither of these compounds commanded a great deal of interest. Eventually it was shown by staining techniques that while DNA was always present in the nucleus, RNA could be found either in the nucleus, within a small body called the nucleolus or, in larger amounts, throughout the cytoplasm.

RNA and DNA resemble one another very closely chemically. The sugar part of RNA has one more oxygen atom (deoxy in chemical language means simply "without an oxygen"), and instead of thymine, RNA contains another pyrimidine, uracil. Like DNA, RNA is made up of submolecules containing a sugar, a phosphate, and a purine or pyrimidine; these are called ribonucleotides. Unlike DNA, most RNA is not found in the form of a double helix. In fact, when RNA is isolated, it does not generally seem to have much of a shape at all but to be just a tangled, fragile thread.

Stanley never ceased to think of tobacco mosaic virus (TMV) as, above all, a self-replicating molecule. From

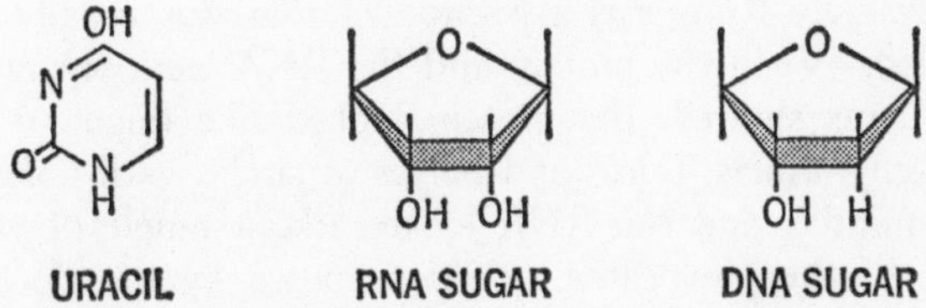

URACIL   RNA SUGAR   DNA SUGAR

Figure 7. The nucleotide of RNA differs only slightly from the nucleotide of DNA. The pyrimidine uracil is found in RNA instead of thymine and the RNA sugar contains one more atom of oxygen than the DNA sugar. (After *Sloan-Kettering Progress Report*.)

the point of view of virus as molecule, the crucial question was what made it work, what gave TMV its specificity, its special and unique ability to make more TMV. Heinz Fraenkel-Conrat, who joined Stanley's laboratory in 1952, was a biochemist by training and, like all biochemists of his time, he thought in terms of proteins. Different strains of tobacco mosaic virus were known which could be distinguished from one another by the differences in the patterns of the scars they traced on the infected leaves. These different strains, Fraenkel-Conrat showed, were slightly different in the make-up of their proteins. No differences could be detected in the RNA that made up the insignificant remainder of the molecule.

Fraenkel-Conrat recalls that he initiated a series of experiments in 1952 in which he tried to produce viral mutants by making chemical changes in the protein of the tobacco mosaic virus. In retrospect, this is a pure Lamarckian misconception, like painting black spots on a white mare so her colt will be piebald, but, as Fraenkel-Conrat clearly remembers, "none of my associates—virus chemists of long standing, these—laughed at me or discouraged my efforts." As it turned out, this was fortunate.

By this time, electron microscope studies by Robley Williams, one of the great experts in this field, showed that TMV was a long rod or cylinder, much longer than T2, but very slender (see Plates 1 and 2). Fraenkel-Conrat worked out methods for isolating the protein for chemical study. The RNA was a by-product that was usually discarded. When the protein and the RNA were separated, Williams showed, the protein looked like fragments of broken washers, thirds and halves of circles with holes in the middle, and the RNA looked like a tangle of yarn. One of the provocative questions posed by the electron micrographs was why the virus was always the same length if it was made up mainly of an assembly of protein units? Sometimes it was shorter—but these particles were not infective—and it was never any longer. This mysteriously determined length of the TMV molecule came to be known as the Stanley unit.

Gerhard Schramm and his co-workers in Tübingen (where Miescher had once worked) showed that if the protein were broken apart gently, it could be coaxed into reaggregating into rods that looked something like TMV. But these rods were never infectious. One day, perhaps with Schramm's experiments stuck in his mind somewhere, Fraenkel-Conrat and his research assistant decided "just for fun" to see what happened when the protein fragments reassembled in the presence of the viral RNA. To their surprise, right under their eyes, the solution of protein and RNA took on a special shine, the opalescence characteristic of the virus. Under the influence of the RNA, the protein gathered into the characteristic TMV particles. When these new particles were viewed under the electron microscope, they looked exactly like ordinary TMV particles. When they were analyzed chemically, they were found to contain protein and RNA in the characteristic ninety-five to five ratio. Most important, when the solution was rubbed on a tobacco leaf, the characteristic signs of infection appeared on the leaf and new virus particles were produced. This time there were headlines in the press about "the creation of life in the test tube," and it did indeed seem that the combination of these two rather ordinary chemicals had fanned some vital unknown spark.

Then, in 1955, Fraenkel-Conrat explored the logic one step further by taking the protein fragments from the TMV of one strain and RNA from another strain. These, too, aggregated to form intact viral particles. By immunological criteria, the protein coat had not been altered chemically by its reassembly around the new RNA core. When these hybrids were rubbed on the tobacco leaf, they, too, were found infective. Curiously, however, the hybrid particles produced only one type of infection, that ordinarily produced by the strain that donated the RNA, never the one from which the protein was derived. Further, when the infective cycle was complete and the new particles emerged, they bore the protein coats of the RNA-donating strain. The nucleic acid of the TMV carried all its power.

The next logical step was taken almost simultaneously by Gierer and Schramm in Tübingen and Fraenkel-Conrat in California. They isolated the nucleic acid from the virus particles and, after scratching the tobacco leaves, rubbed them with the naked viral RNA. Within the usual three days, the unmistakable signs of infection appeared. The nucleic acid alone, absolutely devoid of protein, produced tobacco mosaic disease. RNA alone is much less potent than RNA wrapped in protein—about 1000 times as much is required to produce infection, presumably because the exposed RNA molecule is so easily destroyed. But the infection is the same. Once an intact molecule gets inside a cell, it can organize the characteristic chain of events leading to the production of new progeny TMV, each in an appropriate protein cylinder.

In less than a year, the RNA's of animal viruses were also found to be infective; first polio, then several types of encephalitis, hoof-and-mouth disease, influenza, and a number of others were shown to yield an infective RNA molecule, and to be able to dictate the assembly of a protein jacket.

These studies of Fraenkel-Conrat and Gierer and

Schramm, when they were first reported, were discomfit-ingly out of line with all that was known about the role of RNA in the cell.

In the mid-1940s Jean Brachet of the Free University of Brussels observed that cells synthesizing large amounts of protein, such as those of the pancreas and the liver, stain heavily for RNA. The RNA seemed to be localized in tiny granules, but these were too small to be studied with the light microscope. With the improvement of electron microscopy, George Palade of The Rockefeller Institute was able to identify these granules, tiny spheri-cal particles composed half of RNA and half of protein, which were first called RNP (ribonucleoprotein) particles and later, more simply, ribosomes. Almost all of the cel-lular RNA was found to be associated with the ribosomes, and so it came to be generally accepted that RNA was somehow necessary for making protein. In 1954, the year after Watson and Crick described the structure of DNA, Frederick Sanger at Cambridge University achieved, after a decade, the first complete analysis of the structure of a protein molecule, insulin. Insulin consists of fifty-one amino acids; in different species, Sanger's group found, there are slight characteristic variations in these amino acids, but in the human, or within any other species, only one very specific chain of amino acids functions as insulin.

The Code

By this time, attention was focusing on how the in-formation stored in the DNA molecule was translated into the far different and so precisely demanding lan-guage of the proteins. It was agreed, first, that the infor-mation must be carried primarily in the four bases—adenine, guanine, thymine, and cytosine—since the sug-ars and phosphates were always the same. These bases must somehow specify the code for the amino acids. It could not be a one-to-one ratio; if each base designated one amino acid, only four could be provided for, and at least twenty were needed. If two bases specified one amino acid, there could be a maximum number, using all possible arrangements, of $(4)^2$, or 16, still not quite enough. A code of three provides for $(4)^3$, or 64 possible combinations, which is ample, although somewhat embarrassing in its excess. So, as a result of such calculation, it was proposed that each amino acid is specified by a different nucleotide triplet, which has come to be designated the "codon." More esoteric codes have been suggested, such as overlapping codes in which, if the first amino acid is represented by bases 1, 2, and 3, the second is spelled out by 2, 3, and 4; or four-base codes, or six-base codes, or codes that skip from one helical strand to another, but the triplet continues to be the working hypothesis.

In 1953, the year of Watson and Crick, there was another significant discovery, although its impact was far more gradual. Seymour Cohen, in collaboration with G. R. Wyatt of Canada, found that the DNA of the T-even phages is different from that of other DNA's. Instead of cytosine, it contains a closely related but distinctly different pyrimidine, hydroxy methylcytosine. This compound does not exist in other nucleic acids.

Previously, viruses had not seriously been considered as carrying much in the way of genetic information. In the cliché of the time, the virus was a "complete parasite," a usurper that assumed control of the synthetic processes of the cell and rechanneled them into the production of new viruses. But the presence of the hydroxy methylcytosine suggested that this could not be so. To verify, Cohen gave cytosine labeled with radioactive atoms to E. coli. In virus-infected cells, the cytosine was converted by an enzymatic process to hydroxy methylcytosine, still carrying the distinguishing atomic tag. In uninfected bacteria, this conversion never took place, nor could a single trace of this enzyme system be found. In short, the viral DNA carried the code for this enzyme. Subsequently Cohen and also Kornberg, following this lead, were able to detect a number of viral-induced enzymes concerned with the production of the special viral DNA.

This was important for two reasons. First, the concept that the virus has a metabolic life of its own is a cornerstone of modern viral chemotherapy. This is the subject of a future chapter. Second, the bacteriophage became an extremely valuable, perhaps the indispensable, tool of molecular biology. The question of the moment was how DNA made protein; "one gene—one enzyme" was generally accepted, but what were the steps between? Viruses offered a system by which this might be studied. The total genetic information, the genome, as it came to be called, of the virus was much smaller than that of the cell. The DNA of the T-even phage, for example, is composed of only about 200,000 base pairs, as compared to the ten billion base pairs in the DNA of one human cell. Moreover, the genes of the virus could be turned on at will, almost as simply as throwing a light switch, and, as Delbrück had remarked, each experiment took only a few hours.

In that same year, 1953, Hershey noted that a small amount of RNA was synthesized very rapidly after virus infection. This was a casual observation that attracted little attention. In 1956 Elliot Volkin and Lazarus Astrachan at Oak Ridge examined this new RNA. They isolated it and broke it down into its various bases and discovered that its composition was different from that found in any uninfected bacteria. They measured the proportions of the different bases and found that these proportions were similar to those of the DNA of the T2 phage. Phages, they knew, were made of only protein and DNA; they did not need any RNA. The investigators suggested as one possibility that the RNA was an intermediate from which new phage DNA was made; this they demonstrated, in fact, to be the case. The radioactive labels of the RNA showed up in the DNA of the new virus particles. A few years later the true role of the RNA was uncovered.

The RNA's

During this same incredibly fertile period, Paul Zamecnik and his associates at Harvard University and the Massachusetts General Hospital began to realize that the problem of protein synthesis was too complicated to study in whole cells. Some simpler system was needed. By breaking up cells and spinning them in the ultracentrifuge, they separated cellular components into crude fractions. Radioactive amino acids were prepared and added to each one of these fractions to see which of them contained whatever was needed to make proteins. It turned out that when two of these fractions were put together, the amino acids became linked in polypeptide chains. One of the needed cell fractions contained the ribosomes, long suspected to be involved in protein production. The other fraction required for protein synthesis was the supernatant, the lightest, which consisted mostly of soluble molecules. And this fraction, Zamecnik's group discovered, contributed a new sort of RNA, which they called soluble RNA, to distinguish it from the RNA bound into the ribosomes.

Soluble RNA proved to be a relatively small molecule; later investigations have shown that it consists of only about eighty ribonucleotides arrayed in a short strand which folds back upon itself, like a hairpin. This soluble RNA was not uniform, but heterogeneous, consisting of a variety of slightly different molecules. Most interesting of all, every single amino acid had to hook up with one of these soluble RNA molecules before it could become incorporated into the polypeptide chain. And each type of amino acid was linked to a slightly different type of soluble RNA molecule. This linking process was per-

formed by a particular enzyme. There were at least twenty enzymes, each of which, like skillful interpreters of a foreign language, could "recognize" the amino acid and pair it instantly with the appropriate RNA. At the same time and, it is believed, by the same enzyme, a high-energy phosphate is forged onto the amino acid. This supplies the energy for the formation of the peptide bond.

Soluble RNA, transfer RNA, as it came to be called, was soon accepted to be the dictionary of the cell, but its discovery still left unanswered the question of how the amino acids become arranged in a sequence dictated by the DNA of the gene. It was suggested that the RNA of the ribosomes reflected the genetic DNA, forming a template (just as one strand of DNA in the Watson and Crick model forms a template for the formation of a second strand) and that the transfer RNA molecules, with their captive amino acids, lined up along this RNA template to form polypeptide chains. Indeed it could be shown that the newly forming chains of protein were always associated with the ribosomes.

Jacob and Monod were not content with this hypothesis. Ribosomes are very stable cellular components, passed on through generations of cells. On the other hand, they had found in studies of bacterial mating that when a new gene entered the female cell, a new enzyme could be detected almost instantly, and from this first instant it was forming at the maximum rate. How did the stolid ribosomes incorporate this new information so rapidly?

Conversely, as Jacob and Monod reported in 1960, they grew bacteria in a medium containing enough radioactive phosphorus so that, as the radioactive atoms decayed, they would destroy the DNA, of which they were a part. When this "hot" DNA was passed into a recipient cell during conjugation, the rate of new enzyme production, normal initially, declined rapidly, and its decline paralleled the known explosion rate of the radioactive atoms. In other words, intact DNA had to be present continuously. Ribosomes were not enough.

In 1961 they proposed the existence of a third component in this protein-making system, a transient molecule formed on the DNA template and carrying its message into the cell. At this time they suggested as leading candidate for this role the RNA observed five years previously by Volkin and Astrachan in the virus-infected cell, giving it the name of messenger RNA.

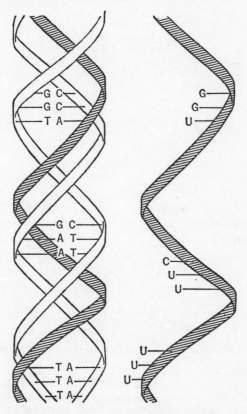

Figure 8. The DNA double helix is the template on which the strand of messenger RNA forms.

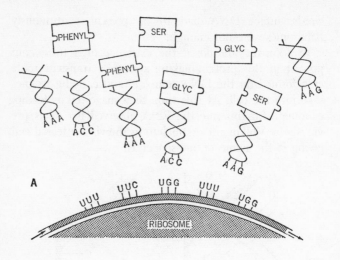

A

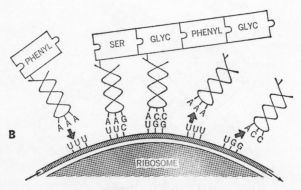

B

Figure 8 a and b. The messenger RNA (a) contains a sequence of base pairs complementary to those of the DNA strand that it "copied." The newly formed messenger RNA then moves from the nucleus of the cell to the cytoplasm where it attaches itself (b) to a ribosome. The transfer RNA's, joined to their particular amino acids, gather along the messenger RNA on the ribosome. The order

The crucial experiment that proved the messenger RNA hypothesis was carried out at the California Institute of Technology at Pasadena, where Delbrück finally settled, using the T-even phage system he had introduced some twenty years before. In keeping with the old tradition, the investigators were Sydney Brenner of Cambridge, Jacob of Paris, and Meselson of California. *E. coli* were grown for several generations on a medium containing heavy isotopes of nitrogen and carbon until they had produced a whole stable of heavy ribosomes. Then the bacteria were moved to a fresh medium where they were infected with T2 and, at the same moment, given a pulse of radioactive phosphorus. When the ribosomes were col-

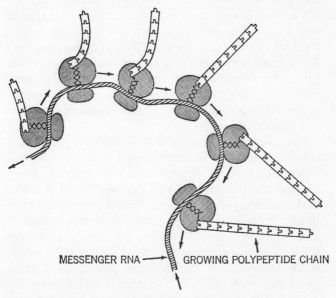

MESSENGER RNA ⟶   GROWING POLYPEPTIDE CHAIN

in which they assemble is presumably dictated by a matching of the sequence of bases along the ribosome and in one area of the transfer RNA molecule. As the amino acids form a peptide chain, the transfer RNA molecules are released. The same messenger RNA molecule is usually "read" by a number of ribosome units simultaneously. (Drawings a and b after drawings in *Scientific American*.)

lected from the cells, they did not contain any of the radioactive phosphorus; yet new protein was forming on these old ribosomes. But in conjunction with the old ribosomes and the new protein there was found a newly formed transient molecule of phosphorus-labeled RNA, the messenger.

The ribosome, it is now known, consists of two particles joined together, one slightly larger than the other, and, according to electron micrographs, the long molecule of messenger RNA appears to be threaded between these two particles. Five or more of the ribosome units move along a molecule of RNA at the same time, "reading" it. Only at the moment that the messenger RNA is in contact with a ribosome can the soluble RNA, or transfer RNA as it is now more commonly called, bring in its amino acid. Presumably, although this is not yet proven, the link between the transfer RNA and the messenger RNA depends also on the system of complementary base pairs. The formation of a protein molecule takes place with incredible speed, in fractions of a second. The messenger RNA is read by two or three groups of ribosomes and then destroyed.

The discovery of messenger RNA added a new dimension to Zamecnik's protein-making system. Investigators from the Pasteur Institute showed that if deoxyribonuclease (the enzyme that destroys DNA) is added to the cell-free system, the formation of new protein stops almost immediately. Apparently DNA "contaminants" were supplying the information for enough messenger RNA to keep the system producing. Marshall Nirenberg of the United States Public Health Service added T_2-inspired messenger RNA to the extracts and discovered a prompt pickup in protein synthesis. In co-operation with Fraenkel-Conrat's group, he took the infectious RNA of the tobacco mosaic virus and put it into the cell-free extract from *E. coli*. The same prompt stimulation was seen; protein production increased seventy-five fold. Viral RNA was playing the role of messenger RNA, and, furthermore, it was playing it not in its natural host, the cells of the tobacco leaves, but in bacteria.

Nirenberg, leaving others to ponder the implications of these findings, raced forward toward a new possibility. If *E. coli* could "read" a foreign message and translate it into protein, perhaps it could also read a totally synthetic one, dictated by man. Several years before, Severo Ochoa of New York University School of Medicine had isolated an enzyme that would link together any combination of ribonucleotides in a non-specific chain. Nirenberg wanted to know exactly what was in the message he was going to transmit and, as the only way that he could be sure, he chose ribonucleotides containing only one of the four bases, uracil. Using Ochoa's enzyme, Nirenberg and Heinrich Matthaei put together an RNA molecule composed entirely of these ribonucleotides. Twenty different ribosome-containing extracts were prepared. Each of these contained all twenty amino acids, one of which, a different one in each case, was marked with a radioactive label. The synthetic RNA, poly-U as it was called, was added to each of these extracts. In nineteen of these test tubes, nothing detectable occurred. But in one of the twenty, the extract into which radioactive phenylalanine had been placed, the investigators detected a newly formed chain of radioactive amino acids. Every one was composed entirely of phenylalanine. Nirenberg and Matthaei had dictated the message: uracil uracil uracil uracil uracil . . . and a clear answer had come back: phenylalanine phenylalanine phenylalanine. . . .

Nirenberg first published his results in August 1961. In the year that followed, his laboratory and that of Ochoa, working independently, were able to work out tentative codes for all of the amino acids, using synthetic messenger RNA. A synthetic made up entirely of adenine, for instance, makes a protein entirely of lysine. If two parts guanine are combined with one part uracil, the protein that is dictated will be composed largely of valine, so it is presumed that the code for valine is GUU, or UUG or UGU (there is not yet any way to tell in which order the RNA bases appear in the synthetic messengers) or perhaps even all three, since more then one triplet is available to code each amino acid. Similarly, AGU seems to code for glutamic acid. Normal hemoglobin contains glutamic acid; sickle cell hemoglobin contains valine, and the difference between the two seems to be simply the replacement of one uracil by one adenine, in a molecule that, since it dictates a polypeptide chain 300 amino acids long, must contain at least 900 bases.

As Tatum has cautioned, it is pretentious and premature to say that we know the language of life. Only a comparatively few proteins have been analyzed completely, and not one single biological sequence of protein-making nucleic acid. We are far from understanding even one sentence, much less a paragraph, and we are very far from the whole story. But it is fair to say that we have learned some of the ABC's.

7   The Bacteriophage

It is no longer so fashionable to debate the difference between the living and the non-living. Self-replication and the ability for adaptive change would certainly be among the generally recognized characteristics of living things. Yet some of these properties, or similar ones, can be found among non-living substances. In any case, no matter where one draws the line, it is very difficult not to think of the bacteriophage as alive. In the first place, its physical structure is so marvelous. Unlike a particle of TMV or of polio, which seems to be one nucleoprotein molecule, T-even is fashioned of at least six separate proteins. First, there is the hexagonal head, made up of repeating units of one type of protein. Then there is the tail, most of the details of which were revealed only a few years ago by the electron microscopy of Sydney Brenner and Robert Horne at the Cavendish Laboratory. (See Plates 3 and 4.) The tail consists of a hollow core encased in a contractile sheath also composed of submolecules which seem to be arranged in a helix. Within this sheath, perhaps with one attached to each submolecule, are some units of ATP (adenosinetriphosphate), a storage depot for the high energy phosphate that provides the power for almost all biological activity. At the very tip of the tail and perpendicular to it is the base plate, which looks like a six-pointed star. From the six points radiate six long fibers which when at rest apparently fold back along the sheath.

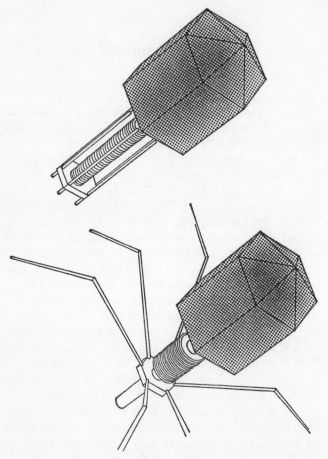

Figure 9. Model of the T-even bacteriophage showing the hexagonal head and the remarkable tail, with its contractile sheath, inner core, base plate, and tail fibers. The lower picture shows the "triggered" phage with sheath contracted. (After drawing in *Scientific American*.)

The Encounter

Encounters between phages and bacteria take place fortuitously, the phage, despite its sperm-like tail, having no innate motility. Bacterial cells have two outer layers, a thin membrane on the inside and a thick wall on the outside. Built into the outer layer are a number of receptor sites, each specific for a different virus. If a bacterium is susceptible to many types of virus, as most are, its cell wall is a mosaic of different receptor sites. Wolfhard Weidel in Tübingen has shown that receptor sites can be chemically extracted from the cell walls. When purified, the receptor substance proves to be complicated mixtures of proteins, fats, and various sugars, combined into a giant molecule which, under the electron microscope, looks like a round pellet. If mixtures of phage are exposed to mixtures of the receptor sites of susceptible cells, phages and receptors will combine and the phages can be seen, by electron microscopy, with the round receptor pellets stuck to the ends of their tails. These phages, corked shut, are no longer infectious.

It appears to be the tail fibers of the phage that attach it to the receptor site of the cell; isolated tail fibers will adsorb to bacteria and will even serve to form bridges between them, causing them to clump together. The tail fibers draw the base plate to the surface of the cell and fix it there. Then the tail protein contracts, using for this contraction the ATP with which it has providently supplied itself. This contraction forces the hollow tail core through the cell wall and through the cell membrane, like a microsyringe.

This DNA is a very long molecule, some 650 times as long as the protein head in which it is contained. A single molecule, it takes the form of the double helix proposed by Watson and Crick, with adenine pairing with thymine and guanine with the unusual hydroxy methylcytosine.

Figure 10. The length of the bacteriophage DNA shown in relationship to the phage head in which it is stored.

Also part of this DNA are submolecules of glucose which are attached to the hydroxy methylcytosine; in T2, seventy-five per cent of the hydroxy methylcytosines have glucose attached, in T4, 100 per cent.

Associated with this DNA inside the head of the phage and injected with it into the bacterial cell are some relatively small polypeptides. There are also some larger protein molecules which go by the rather inelegant name of gut protein. The function of this protein, which makes up about three per cent of the total phage protein, is not known. Aaron Bendich points out that no DNA has ever been isolated completely free of protein and offers evidence that peptides, small groups of amino acids, occur from time to time along the DNA molecule. These, he suggests, may serve as punctuation for the genetic code, telling the messenger DNA where to start or stop reading the particular sequence of nucleotides that dictates one protein chain. Also, Bendich says, these same peptides might serve as the hinges along which the relatively stiff

DNA molecule might be folded for packing into the phage head. This question of the packing is, of course, a subject of much interest because of its great efficiency; some sort of modified fire-hose assembly is generally favored. In any case, once the phage is triggered, this DNA with its mysterious associated protein slips into the bacterial cell.

By this time, changes have already begun within the besieged cell. The attachment of the T-even phage arrests cell division and inhibits synthesis of cellular DNA and RNA. These events take place even if the bacteria are exposed only to phage "ghosts"—empty protein coats devoid of DNA. From the moment the long molecule of phage DNA enters the cell, all metabolic activities are directed toward the production of new virus. First, as Volkin and Astrachan showed, the fleeting molecules of messenger RNA form. From this messenger RNA, a whole new set of proteins is run off. One of these "early" proteins is the gut protein. All of the others that have been identified are concerned with the production of viral DNA, such as the enzymes concerned with making hydroxy methylcytosine, first detected by Cohen. Kornberg and his group have also identified some virus-induced enzymes, including a DNA polymerase which causes new strands of DNA to form along the templates of the old strands (the bacteria have a DNA polymerase, too, but that of the virus is slightly different); an enzyme that attaches glucose to the DNA molecule (this is done after the molecule is formed); and an enzyme that breaks down any cytosine that has not been converted to hydroxy methylcytosine. This last enzyme is apparently the way that the phage insures that its DNA will contain only the unusual pyrimidine, since either would fit the template just as well.

All available nucleotides are used for viral DNA. A cell in a vigorously growing bacterial colony will divide every twenty minutes, so it usually has a good supply of free nucleotides on hand for its own purposes. But these are not enough. The DNA of the bacteria is broken apart and converted; the bacterial chromosomes begin to disintegrate within two or three minutes after infection. Messenger RNA is torn up and reprocessed for viral DNA. If the cell is superinfected with more T-even phages (tagged with radioactive phosphorus to distinguish them from the first invaders), these superinfecting phage fragments are cannibalized, their labeled nucleotides spotting the DNA of the new phage progeny. Another intriguing question among the many left unanswered is how the newly forming phage DNA is protected from the holocaust of destruction surrounding it.

Production of these early enzymes starts about two or three minutes after infection and lasts for about seven minutes. During this period apparently all the enzymes that are needed for viral DNA replication are produced. If an experimenter inhibits all protein synthesis at the moment of cell infection (this can be done readily by adding the antibiotic chloramphenicol), no new viral DNA is formed. If protein synthesis is inhibited after the "early" enzymes are formed, viral DNA is produced in normal amounts, although no coat protein can be made. Shortly after DNA synthesis starts, the synthesis of "early" proteins stops. These two events are linked together. If DNA synthesis is prevented by irradiation, the production of "early" proteins continues for as long as half an hour or more, as it does in various mutants that cannot make more DNA. Similarly, if no viral DNA is formed, the coat proteins never appear, and in mutants that are defective in DNA synthesis the amount of late protein is proportional to the amount of new viral DNA.

At about eight minutes after infection, viral DNA (identifiable by the hydroxy methylcytosine) begins to accumulate within the cell.

As the viral DNA collects, it forms in pools, apparently occupying the vacuoles that previously accommodated the bacterial chromosomes, of which there are usually two or three or four in each bacterial cell. Eventually, these pools coalesce. It is within these DNA pools that the long threads of viral DNA recombine with one another and, as Delbrück and Hershey showed many years before, different strains and mutants of the same strain will undergo this sort of recombination, making it possible to map the bacteriophage chromosome.

The synthesis of coat protein starts at about the same time as the synthesis of viral DNA, and by the time enough viral DNA has formed to supply thirty or forty phages, complete particles begin to appear, marking the formal end of the "eclipse" period. DNA and coat protein continue to appear in parallel, as if from two efficient production lines. The DNA supply always stays a little ahead of the demand, with thirty or forty "phage units" always available, mating, in the pool.

The way in which the DNA and the various proteins are finally assembled into complete particles is a subject of current interest to many investigators, among whom is Edward Kellenberger of the University of Geneva. Kellenberger calculates that the DNA in the phage head is fifteen times as compact as the DNA in the viral pool, so that one of the steps in the maturation of the virus must be a condensation of the nucleic acid. Searching thin sections of infected *E. coli* with the electron microscope, Kellenberger has found examples of phage DNA folded into little hexagonal-shaped packages with no visible protein surrounding them.

Just as TMV workers some years ago wondered how that viral particle always assumed the same length, "the Stanley unit," students of the bacteriophage are curious about what dictates the length of the tail. Sewell Champe of Purdue suggests that a free loop of DNA might be left protruding from the assembly in the head and that the tail proteins might form around this. This free end of DNA, he points out, would greatly facilitate passage of the giant molecule through this small lumen of the tail core at the time of injection.

In any case, no matter how it is accomplished, the viral assembly system is remarkably efficient and some ninety per cent of the new viral DNA ends up protein packaged.

Eventually, after about twenty or thirty minutes, depending on various combinations of phages, bacteria, and environment, the cell wall lyses. This is caused by the production of the viral-directed enzyme lysozyme, and has nothing to do with the large accumulation of phage particles inside the cells, as was once thought. If all protein synthesis is halted after the lysozyme is formed, lysis still occurs even though no complete particles are ever made. Conversely, in mutants that cannot form lysozyme, viral particles pack the cell, but they cannot escape unless the wall is ruptured artificially.

When the cell bursts, 200 or 300 viral particles spill out, each one of them ready to begin again the exact same sequence of events.

Genetic Fine Structure

Because of the facility and rapidity with which the bacteriophage can be manipulated and the relatively limited size of its genetic information, it is possible to carry out chromosome mapping experiments of a complexity and scope impossible even with one-celled organisms. And these experiments have had and are continuing to have a profound influence on the course of molecular biology. For instance, Mendelian genetics had conceived of the gene as an indivisible, discrete unit, a bead on a string. But if the new biology was right, there were no beads, just a long string, divisible anywhere along its length.

The first to put this notion to a rigorous test was Seymour Benzer of Purdue University, using the bacteriophage. For the purposes of his experiments, Benzer selected a series of mutants of T4 which could reproduce on *E. coli* B but could not grow at all on *E. coli* K. On B, these mutants could be distinguished from the "normal" or "wild" type T4 by the type of plaque or clearing they produced in the bacterial lawn; the mutants made large clear plaques, the wild type, small fuzzy ones. To isolate the mutants, one simply spread virus particles over a bacterial colony in a solution so dilute that it was very unlikely that more than one particle would infect a single cell. When an abnormal plaque formed, the mutant virus particles that had formed it could be collected from that clearing on the gel. These mutants in turn, like their progenitors, made large clear plaques on the B strain and could not grow on the K strain. Benzer found, however, that if wild-type phage were multiplying in the K cells at the same time, the mutants would also multiply, producing more of their own kind. Apparently the wild-type T4 made something that the mutant did not, just as wild-type *Neurospora* made something that its mutants did not. If the gene were a bead on a string, the bead would either be there or not. But if the gene were a sequence of information, small changes—"typographical errors"—could occur anywhere in this sequence. Hershey and Delbrück had shown a decade before that phage can mate so that two particles with mutations in two different genes can recombine to form a wild type. Benzer now set out to discover if phage can have different mutations within the same gene and if two of these can also recombine to form a wild type.

The experiments were simple. Two mutants isolated from different abnormal B plaques would be mixed together and spread over a K 12 colony. If only mutant phages were present, no plaques would appear on the K colony. If mutants could combine to make wild type, plaques would appear. And plaques did appear, not often but frequently enough to be seen and to be counted. (Again the great advantage of working with phages was that literally millions of progeny could be studied in each

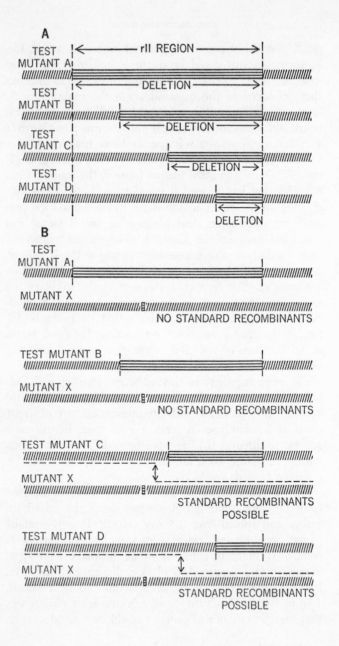

A

TEST
MUTANT A

rII REGION

DELETION

TEST
MUTANT B

DELETION

TEST
MUTANT C

DELETION

TEST
MUTANT D

DELETION

B

TEST
MUTANT A

MUTANT X

NO STANDARD RECOMBINANTS

TEST MUTANT B

MUTANT X

NO STANDARD RECOMBINANTS

TEST MUTANT C

MUTANT X

STANDARD RECOMBINANTS
POSSIBLE

TEST MUTANT D

MUTANT X

STANDARD RECOMBINANTS
POSSIBLE

experiment.) Phages with mutations within the same gene could recombine to make a "normal" gene. To use Benzer's own simile, it was like taking two tape recordings of a message, each message being one gene. Each tape contained a slight error, but in a different place, and splicing them together, one could get a perfect tape. To carry the analogy a little further, it can be seen that if one error is at the beginning of a message and one at the end, cutting and splicing the tapes almost anywhere along their length will produce a perfect result, but if the mistakes are close together, many random recombinations or splicings can take place without a perfect tape being produced. Of course, if the errors overlap, there is no way that they can correct one another.

Repeating the experiments over and over, Benzer, who first reported his results in 1955, has been able to isolate some 5000 different mutants and, by observing the frequency with which they recombine to make a perfect tape, he has been able to map them. Some of these mutants involve comparatively large segments of the gene, as if one whole part of the message were wiped out or censored. There are about fifty of these, all of which have been located in relation to one another along the chromosomal segment. When a new mutant is found, it is tested first against these large mutations; a recombinant can occur only if the large mutation does not overlap the small one.

Figure 11. By attempting recombination experiments with various known Test Mutants, Benzer is able to locate the position of an unknown mutation within the bacteriophage gene. Figure 11 A shows four standard Test Mutants each of which have deletions of large portions of the rII region, or gene. As Figure 11 B indicates, Mutant X cannot recombine with either Test Mutant A or Test Mutant B to form a "correct" or standard gene, since the "errors" in A and B overlap with the "error" (or mutation) in Mutant X. On the other hand, recombinations with Test Mutants C and D are possible which will yield phage with a standard genetic message in this region. By such experiments using many Test Mutants, it is possible to locate an intragenic mutation very precisely. (After a drawing in *Scientific American*.)

Then when the mutant is generally located along the sequence, it is tested against others in the same area. Thus it has been possible to map mutations that seem to be no more than a single nucleotide in size, and even these mutants can recombine. So DNA, at least this particular segment of this particular DNA, is a straight linear message.

In the course of mapping the "fine structure of the gene," as he calls it, Benzer found that some pairs of mutants could also help one another in the way that wild type and a mutant can, without recombination taking place. When he mapped these mutants, he found that invariably those that were mutually helpful were mutants whose "errors," whether large or small, were located in different halves of the mapping area. The "gene" he was studying, he concluded, actually consists of two segments, A and B, which appear to have two separate functions. If one virus can give complete A instructions and one complete B instructions, both A and B, whatever they are, can be produced normally and used mutually by the two viruses to produce new particles. But A and B must be complete to function. Benzer proposed the name "cistron" for these different segments of the DNA molecule, each of which presumably dictates one complete amino-acid sequence, and the classic "one gene—one enzyme" slogan of Beadle and Tatum took on its present ponderous form: "one cistron—one polypeptide chain."

Benzer's two cistrons appear to make up about one per cent of the phage DNA, or some 2000 base pairs. Mutations do not occur evenly along this sequence. There are certain "hot spots" where spontaneous mutations occur over and over again, and there are small areas where a mutation never occurs. Certain chemicals cause mutations at some loci and not at others. It seems certain that these variations in the susceptibility to change are a direct result of the varying patterns of nucleotide pairs, and Benzer's studies are now reaching the point where he can make some deductions about the actual arrangements of the bases along this segment of the T4 DNA molecule. It is one of the ironies of biology, however, that no one has yet succeeded in isolating the protein products of the A and B cistrons of the T4 bacteriophage.

The Genome of T4

Recently Robert S. Edgar of the California Institute of Technology, which has been the center of so many of these studies, and Richard Epstein, now at the University of Geneva, have reported a series of studies that have excited widespread admiration and delight. Using the familiar T4, they have isolated a number of mutants, all of which are what is known as "conditional lethals." This means simply that the mutations are fatal under some circumstances but not under others, just as the mutations in *Neurospora* were fatal in the simple medium but not in the enriched; as Edgar puts it, it's a way of having your cake and eating it, too. Epstein's mutants, like Benzer's, will grow in one host (a variety of *E. coli* K) but not in another (*E. coli* B). Edgar's mutants are temperature-sensitive or, more precisely, heat-sensitive. Apparently small mutations, "typographical errors" in the DNA code, can produce proteins that are able to function under optimum conditions but, like any piece of defective equipment, are less reliable under strain. The idea that certain enzymes can act only at certain temperatures is not a new one. The Siamese cat, for instance, is dark only on his tail, feet, and the tip of his nose because only these points in his body are cool enough for the temperature-sensitive color-producing genes to function. Edgar has now managed to isolate hundreds of separate mutations (together Edgar and Epstein have more than a thousand), spread all around the bacteriophage chromosome, that will halt growth at temperatures slightly higher than normal. These provide an exceptional tool: he can grow the same

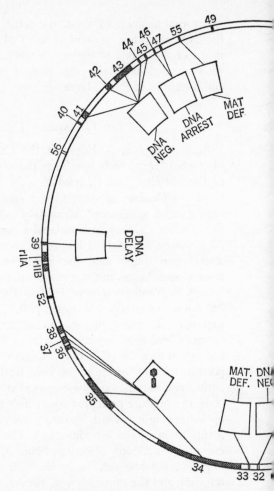

Figure 12. Gene map of T4 shows the relative positions of the 60 genes identified so far. The boxes within the circle show the effects of mutations in these genes, including the production of particles without heads or without tails, failures in the synthesis of DNA or failure of virus maturation. Minimum length is known for some of these genes (black segments) but not for others (gray segments). (After a drawing in *Scientific American*.)

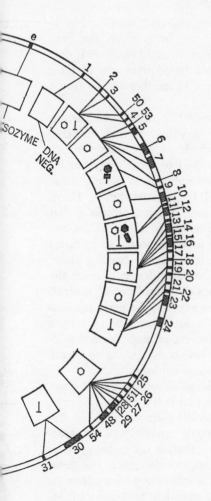

mutant simultaneously at two different temperatures to
pinpoint what happens in one host, when the gene
"works," which does not happen in another, when it does
not; also he can move cells infected with one of these
mutants from one temperature to another and so turn a
particular gene on or off.

The isolation and characterization of mutants such as
Edgar's and Epstein's is a very tedious and time-con-
suming task involving hundreds of experiments which
must be very carefully monitored to catch every mutant
that appears and to study recombinations among them.
One day Epstein cajoled CIT graduate student Harris
Bernstein into helping him pick plaques, promising that
any mutants he found would be named after him. So, as a
result of a rather attenuated pun, they came to be called
the "amber" mutants, Bernstein being a burning stone,
amber being a stone that burns, and Bernstein being the
object of their gratitude. Thus the term "amber" mutant,
usually written *am* to make it more cryptic and authorita-
tive, has made its way into the formal scientific literature
and will undoubtedly be the source of much learned speculation by future scientific historians seeking to recon-
struct the golden age of American virology.

One of the astonishing things about the chromosome
map of Edgar and Epstein is that it is a circle. This does
not mean that the DNA actually forms a circle—as Edgar says, the chromosome could equally well be represented by a square—but rather that, in the course of mapping experiments, if an investigator designates one gene,
any gene, as A, and another, a middling distance from A,
according to recombination statistics, is designated M,
and then he works, still following the recombination
criteria, farther on past M toward Z, he once more approaches A. In other words, there is no end to the link-
ages. A few years ago Jacob and Monod demonstrated, in
bacterial conjugation experiments, that the chromosome
of *E. coli* is also a circle, and some investigators now haz-

ard a guess that all genetic material will prove to be in such a form.

Figure 12 shows the result of these mapping studies. The numbers 1 through 49 on Figure 12 indicate the various cistrons that have been identified so far, their sizes, and their distances from one another according to the recombination experiments. The genes vary greatly in length. The gene for lysozyme, according to these mapping experiments, has turned out to be just about the right size (about 450 nucleotide pairs) to make a protein about 150 amino acids long, which is about the length of lysozyme as isolated from the infected cell. As can be seen, about half of the chromosome is now mapped.

The map shows in a schematic form what these cistrons do and how they were found. Cistron 1, for example, has to do with DNA synthesis; when there is a mutation in this cistron, the amber mutant cannot make DNA in the non-permissive host. Cistron 10 has something to do with tail structures since the phages with mutations in this gene have heads but cannot make tails in the non-permissive host.

One of the particularly interesting findings that show up on this map is that genes involved in the same sort of activity occur, generally speaking, in clusters. For example, the cistrons which are concerned with the synthesis of DNA, and so presumably control early protein synthesis, are together at the top of the circular map. DNA synthesis starts only after the "early proteins" are completed. John Buchanan at the Massachusetts Institute of Technology has shown that mutations in gene 42 affect the synthesis of the enzyme first detected by Cohen, which converts cytosine to hydroxy methylcytosine. Viruses lacking this enzyme cannot make viral DNA.

The cistron for lysozyme lies between genes 49 and 1 of Edgar's mutants. The cistrons rIIA and rIIB are those studied by Benzer. Genes 20 to 24 and 30 and 31 have to do with the bacteriophage heads since in non-permissive hosts, or at higher temperatures, only tail particles are formed by the mutants. Recently Brenner has shown that cistron 23 dictates the structure for head protein. Phages with mutations in genes 34 through 38 look normal but are not infective and so are believed to lack tail fibers. The gene for host range, mapped years ago by Delbrück and Hershey, is probably located in or near gene 37, which is also satisfying since it is the tail-fiber structure that is believed to control host range. Mutants deficient in genes 41 through 45 cannot make DNA.

As Edgar has noted, there seem to be more cistrons than can be explained by simply calculating the number of new proteins that are needed. For example, there is one cistron for head protein but some seven others are involved in the production of phage heads. Either, Edgar postulates, there must be a number of still undetected proteins in the finished virus that serve as nuts and bolts to hold the structure together or, more likely, there are a lot of genes that are involved with assembly. (When gene 20 is defective, for instance, the protein subunits of the head assemble in the form of long cylindrical tubes instead of forming hexagons.) If the product of these genes can be identified, it will be biology's first entree into the understanding (in molecular terms) of questions of morphogenesis, the way in which living things form their various components and take on their characteristic shapes.

The clustering of the genes into different functional groups makes it appear as if the information is taken off the cistron in an ordered sequence; this is confirmed by recent studies of Sol Spiegelman's showing that the messenger RNA found in the cell in the early stages of T-even infection is different from that isolated later on. In other words, enzymes and other proteins are not simply produced all at the same time to be used as needed in the course of infection, but the genes dictate not only what proteins will be formed but when they will be formed. Also, as Champe points out, they exert a control on how much will be formed. Head membrane, for instance, consists of about 1000 subunits, while the six tail fibers together probably contain no more than thirty; yet no great excess of protein is produced. Each cistron is under some sort of quantitative regulation.

So here, posted in a very concrete form, is the question of how the expression of the DNA is controlled, coordinated, and modulated, as it must be to produce cellular differentiation and adaptation and to effect the complex interactions of proteins—in other words, the processes included under the general heading of living. Most observers agree that these questions of modulation and morphogenesis are the next great themes of modern biology.

8 Lysogeny

Forty years ago when the controversy of spontaneous generation circled, hovered, and came momentarily to rest on the bacteriophages, the issue most difficult to resolve was lysogeny. Lysogeny is caused by the sudden release from a cell of viruses which may have remained latent within it for tens and thousands of cellular generations. From the beginning, this phenomenon has been of special interest to the "French school" of bacteriophage research, particularly those scientists at the Pasteur Institute in Paris where once before a similar question was put so brilliantly to rest.

D'Hérelle, in the 1920s, claimed lysogeny represented merely a special instance of symbiosis between two living things, cell and protobios, or bacteriophage. Bordet, his old antagonist, held, on the contrary, that the lysogenic bacteria did not yield an autonomous agent but simply a noxious substance that might, under appropriate circumstances, provoke other cells to become similarly ill and make more of the same poison, so spreading it through the culture. F. M. Burnet of the University of Melbourne, who was just beginning about that time to make the weight of his opinions felt, pointed out that the relationship between the lysogenic bacterium and its phage was actually the best possible one, especially for the phage, and suggested that this was probably the most likely condition of existence for all viruses. Rampaging infection in which the virus destroyed its host and so itself, would appear, in this light, to be the exception rather than the rule. Eugene Wollman of the Pasteur Institute, seeing even a little deeper into the phenomenon, reflected—and this was long before Stanley or Hershey or Watson or Crick —"the two notions of heredity and infection which seem so completely distinct and in some ways incompatible . . . almost merge under certain characteristics."

In some bacteria, such as *Salmonella* and *Staphylococcus*, almost every strain is lysogenic for at least one and often several bacteriophages. Wollman and his wife Elisabeth began a quiet systematic study of lysogeny, establishing which strains of bacteria conceal viruses and which do not and the circumstances under which they may best be cultured. This work was interrupted in December 1943 when the Wollmans were seized by the Nazis in Paris and a few weeks later deported to Germany. Official records cannot be found as to whether or not they survived the journey to Buchenwald; it is generally thought not since it was unusually cold that winter. In any case, if they arrived, they were sent directly to the gas chamber since they were old and ill and unable to perform useful work. Their three children escaped, among them Elie Wollman, who has won such a brilliant reputation for his studies with Jacob and Monod in the study of bacterial genetics at the Pasteur Institute.

After the war was over, the Paris work on bacteriophage was resumed, at this time under the leadership of André Lwoff. Taking up where the Wollmans left off, Lwoff established that lysogenic cells do not casually secrete an occasional bacteriophage, but that in the course of lysogeny a whole burst of virus particles is produced with the concomitant destruction of the responsible cell. Next he showed that if he exposed certain types of lysogenic bacteria to radiation or to chemicals, every single cell in the colony would produce phages. Induction, as this came to be called, was very useful technically since investigators of lysogeny no longer had to wait for the one bacterium in a million to produce phage spontaneously. The fact that every single cell in a particular col-

ony, when suitably induced, could liberate a virus was
also of theoretical importance since it proved that the
release of bacteriophage was a built-in hereditary property of the bacteria, not an aberration or a disease.

By 1953, Lwoff was able to link lysogeny and infection
—the temperate and the virulent phages—within one con-
ceptual framework. When a bacterial virus enters a bacterial cell, it "decides" whether or not to lysogenize, depending on virus, host, and other, unknown conditions.
If it chooses virulence, it enters what Lwoff calls the vegetative state, during which it produces more phage. If
it chooses lysogeny, it disappears within the cell and becomes part of it; it can be passed on through countless
cell divisions, and thousands of daughter cells may acquire
it, not as a virus but as a property. This property, the
hereditary ability to produce bacteriophage, Lwoff gave
the name "prophage."

When the balance between prophage and host is upset,
Lwoff showed, either by induction or "spontaneously,"
then the prophage becomes a vegetative phage and enters
on a replicative or virulent cycle, as if it had just arrived
through the cell wall. At the end of this cycle the cell
bursts and releases hundreds of phage progeny, each of
which will in turn "decide" whether to infect or to lysogenize.

Since, as Lwoff showed, every cell of a lysogenic colony
contains prophage, the prophage must replicate every
time the bacterial chromosome does, which suggested
that it might actually be part of the chromosome. Joshua
Lederberg and his wife, who became interested in this
question, realized that it could be answered with a bacterial cell that was lysogenic and that also mated. They
sought and finally found a bacteriophage that lysogenized
E. coli K 12, the bacterial cell in which mating was originally observed. By mating lysogenic bacteria with non-
lysogenic bacteria they were able to demonstrate that the
prophage entered the recipient cell right along with the

chromosome, and, moreover, that it occupied its own particular place on the chromosome. Soon after, fifteen other
phages, all of which are lysogenic for K 12, were found,
and all these too had their precisely allocated positions
among the bacterial genes.

It is believed that the temperate phages can attach
themselves to the bacterial chromosome because they
have areas on their own chromosomes that correspond to
these points of attachment, presumably because of identical sequences of nucleotides in both sets of DNA. Therefore, exchanges can take place between phage and bacterial chromosome, just as they can in recombination in
viruses or mating in bacteria or crossing-over in the
gametes. As a result of such exchanges, the phage chromosome becomes inserted in that of the bacterium. If the
phage undergoes a mutation in the attachment area, it
loses its ability to lysogenize and is condemned forever to
a life of virulence.

Mutations may also occur in other parts of the chromosome of the temperate viruses, and these, like mutations
in the T-even phage, can change their ability to replicate
and produce more viruses. Lysogenic bacteria bearing defective prophages cannot be induced to produce viruses,
but if they are superinfected with "whole" phage of the
same strain and then induced, the whole viruses help
the defective ones to mature. Then inside some of the
protein overcoats of the particles that are released will
be packaged the defective genome of the mutant viruses,
and the bacteria that receive these will also be unable to
produce bacteriophages.

When the position of the lambda phage, the one first
discovered by the Lederbergs, was mapped, it was found
that its allocated position on the bacterial chromosome
was right next to the bacterial gene that determined
whether or not the bacterium could utilize galactose, a
type of sugar. In the shorthand of bacterial genetics, bacteria that can use galactose, a common genetic marker,

are designated Gal +, while those that cannot are Gal —.
When lambda phages are released from K 12 Gal + bacteria, a small proportion of them—about one in a million
—carry with them the Gal + gene, and the bacterial cells
which they infect thereby acquire not only lambda prophage but the ability to utilize galactose. If these cells,
in turn, are induced to produce phages, a large proportion
of the phages they release will carry the Gal + gene. In
other words, the gene seems to be picked up from time to
time by accident from the bacterial chromosome, but once
this has happened the bacterial gene becomes almost a
part of the phage, replicating with the phage genome.
There is evidence, however, that the phages that pick up
the Gal gene have to jettison some of their own genetic
baggage. Recombination tests indicate that as much as
one fourth of the regular phage genome is missing in
these lambda. They can replicate but only in the presence
of other helper phages that produce the materials that
they are lacking.

In addition to the bacterial genes they may acquire as
an incidental part of their baggage, the prophage themselves confer certain new characteristics on their host.
The first of these to be observed was immunity. If a lysogenic cell releases phages into a colony of other bacteria
lysogenic for the same phages, nothing will happen at all.
A cell carrying the prophage for any particular virus is
completely immune to infection by another virus of that
same type, which is why lysogeny can be detected only
if a sensitive "indicator" strain of bacteria is present. The
phages can enter the cell, it has been found, but they
cannot multiply in it. This immunity seems to be caused
by something, undoubtedly a protein, produced under
the direction of the phage. This unidentified protein acts
on the genes of the incoming phages and somehow turns
them off. It is perhaps the same substance that keeps the
original prophage from multiplying in the cell and so
makes the "decision" for lysogeny. In any case, the bac-

terial geneticists suspect that, whatever it is, it is closely related to the materials produced by certain genes of the bacterial cell that turn on and off the production of particular enzymes and, in this way, are powerful regulators of the entire cellular economy. As such, the immunity substance will be under increasingly intensive future scrutiny.

Another property that a lysogenic phage may bestow upon its host was discovered by V. J. Freeman at the University of Washington in his studies of a phage lysogenic for the diphtheria bacillus. All the ugly symptoms of diphtheria, the "throat distemper" that was such a frequent cause of childhood mortality only a few decades ago, are caused not by direct effects of the bacilli themselves, it has long been known, but by the toxin they produce. This toxin is a complex protein and, Freeman discovered, the bacillus makes this complex protein only when it is infected by a particular temperate bacteriophage. Without its prophage, the diphtheria bacillus is completely harmless.

In 1957 Hisao Ueteke, working in Luria's laboratory, discovered that following infection with a lysogenic phage, *Salmonella* became immunologically different, that is, a new antigen appeared on the surface of the cell. (Antigens are simply substances that provoke the formation of antibodies, and any cell surface is made up of a large number of different antigens, all of which, like all proteins, are genetically determined.) The antigen appears on the surface of *Salmonella* almost immediately after infection and persists as long as the phage is in the cell. It bears no immunological relationship to the phage but is an entirely new substance. Actually, as was later found, the antigen appears whether the phages infect or lysogenize. In the former case, the antigen survives only as long as the cell, but in the lysogenic bacterium, it becomes a permanent characteristic passed with the prophage down through the cellular generations.

The F Factor

In his studies on bacterial mating, Lederberg discovered that bacteria have sex, some playing the predetermined role of donor and some of recipient in the transfer of genetic material. "Maleness," he found, is conferred by a component which is known as the fertility factor, or "F." As far as all studies have been able to show, F is composed entirely of DNA. During mating, F may be transferred to the female cell, in which case that cell becomes a male.

The F factor, Jacob and Wollman have shown, may either exist free in the cytoplasm of the male cell, in which case it is usually the only component passed to the female cell during conjugation, or it may attach itself to the bacterial chromosome. At the point at which F attaches—which can be any one of several specific loci—the circular chromosome opens. The free end of the open chromosome is the first to cross the cytoplasmic bridge to penetrate the female cell during mating. The F factor, which is attached to the far end of the chromosome, appears in the female cell only if the entire chromosome has entered. The F factor may disattach itself from the chromosome and, as it does, it may take a gene or two with it, and these then can be transmitted into the recipient female cell along with "maleness." The presence of the F factor changes the surface of the bacterial cell, which is what makes possible the construction of the mating bridge. In other words, F factor is very much like lysogenic phage. Components like sex factor and lysogenic phage, which may or may not form a part of the chromosomes of the bacterial cell and which are not vital to its existence, Jacob and Wollman have given the name of "episomes."

Allan M. Campbell of the University of Rochester has recently postulated, on the basis of convincing evidence, that the chromosomes of both temperate phage and F factor, like the bacterial chromosome, form circles. The little circle, either F factor or phage, comes together tangentially at a specific point with the big circle, the bacterial chromosome. Then both open at just this point so that the two circles join together to make one larger one in which the F factor or phage has become part of the bacterial chromosome. Under other circumstances, the two may separate again, to form a large circle, the bacterial chromosome, and a small one, the episome. Campbell points out that there is actually no reason why other elements of the chromosome should not be able to break away to lead an independent existence. If one thinks about this for very long, it begins to seem a little like spontaneous generation.

Part III

VIRUSES AND DISEASE

9   The Vaccines

Each summer for almost half a century poliomyelitis hung
like a specter over the countryside. To a modern public
benumbed by large figures, its actual death toll was not
high; somewhat more, perhaps, than the number of deaths
among children deemed "acceptable" by proponents of
atomic testing programs but far less than the yearly deaths
in this age group from accidents, cancer, or several other
infectious diseases. But the crippling effects were permanent, and each year hundreds more were condemned by
some bewildering, immutable judgment—no wonder the
primitives thought angry gods were to blame—to a lifetime in splints, braces, wheelchairs, and that most hideous of lifesaving devices, the iron lung.

Infantile paralysis has left a dim trail winding far back
into prehistory, according to the paleopathologists, but it
was not until 1840 that Jacob Heine described it as a separate disease entity. Somewhat later in that century it came
to bear the name poliomyelitis, after "polio," which is
Greek for "gray," and "myelos," which means "marrow,"
because of the characteristic lesions in the spinal cords
of those children examined at autopsy. Forty-four cases
of the disease, the first epidemic, were reported in Stock-
holm in the summer of 1887; in 1894, 132 cases occurred
in Vermont; and in 1905, in Sweden, there was an un-
precedentedly large epidemic of 1031 cases. Ivar Wick-
man, in what is considered one of the early masterpieces
of epidemiology, was able to trace the passage of the
unusually virulent strain of 1905 from one person to another, establishing infantile paralysis conclusively as an

infectious disease. Little more than a decade later, in 1916, the United States was struck by an epidemic that affected more than 27,000 people and killed some 6000. In New York City, where 2000 died that summer from polio, quarantine was imposed and panic-stricken citizens had to be forcibly restrained from flight in scenes reminiscent of the medieval plagues.

Polio Vaccines

Research on polio got off to a very promising start. In 1909, Karl Landsteiner, the great Viennese immunologist who discovered the major blood types and so made transfusions feasible, showed that a filtrate of spinal cord from a fatal human paralytic disease caused a similar fatal paralytic disease when injected into monkeys. Within a year, investigators had established that the agent was a filterable virus, that monkeys surviving one attack were resistant to reinfection, and that when the serum of such survivors was mixed with live virus, the virus was "neutralized" and no longer infective.

After this, the work floundered for almost thirty years and actually, in retrospect, it would seem that those involved in the modern attack on poliomyelitis might have been better off if all the earnest, hopeful, and hard-won achievements of those three decades had never been recorded.

In the first place, despite the early successes, polio was a puzzling disease. There was no simple, revealing pattern of mass infection followed by mass immunity, as in smallpox, for example. Polio, or infantile paralysis, as both of these names indicate, was recognized as such only when it caused paralytic disease, but except for the atypical 1905 epidemic in Sweden there was rarely any history of one person who became paralyzed having been exposed to another person who became paralyzed. Howard Howe, one of the Johns Hopkins team involved in much of the

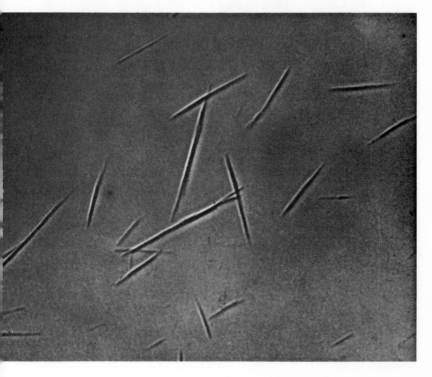

PLATE 1. Crystals of tobacco mosaic virus. Photograph by W. M. Stanley, *American Journal of Botany*, 1937.

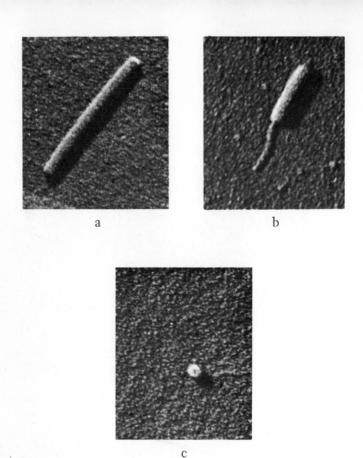

PLATE 2. a) Intact particle of tobacco mosaic virus. b) Particle of virus with some of the protein coat removed to expose the core of ribonucleic acid. c) View of the protein coat material seen end-on. The hole in the center accommodated the molecule of viral RNA. Photograph by Roger G. Hart, *Proceedings of the National Academy, U.S.* 41, 1955.

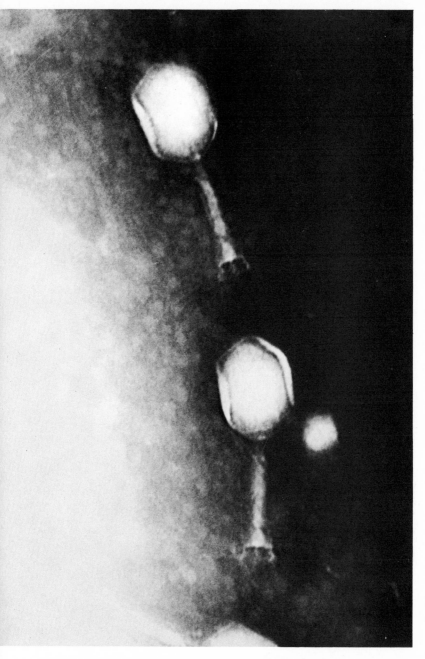

PLATE 3. T2 bacteriophage. Photograph by S. Brenner, R. W. Horne, et. al., *Journal of Molecular Biology*, 1959, Academic Press Inc.

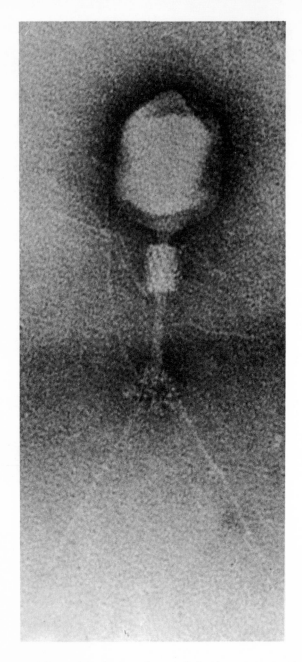

PLATE 4. Triggered T2 bacteriophage, tail sheath contracted and tail fibers released. Photograph by S. Brenner, R. W. Horne, et. al., *Journal of Molecular Biology*, 1959, Academic Press Inc.

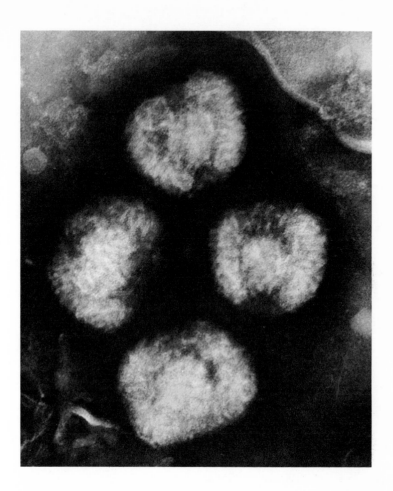

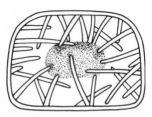

PLATE 5. Particles of vaccinia virus in electron micrograph (top) and drawing (bottom), the dumb-bell-shaped core of DNA and protein surrounded by a lipoprotein envelope. Photograph by R. W. Horne and J. Nagington, *Virology*, 1961. Drawing after a drawing in *Scientific American*.

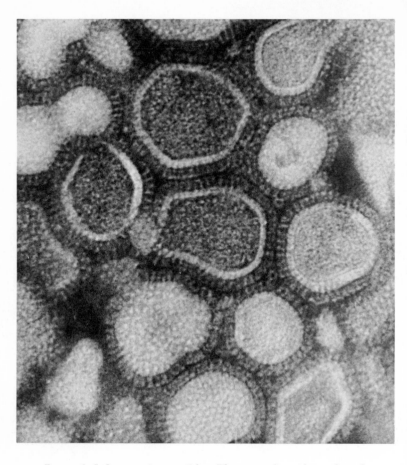

PLATE 6. Influenza virus particles. The external envelope, through which the spikes protrude, encloses an inner helical structure composed of RNA and protein. Photograph by R. W. Horne, A. P. Waterson, P. Wildy, and A. E. Farnham, *Virology*, 1961, Academic Press Inc.

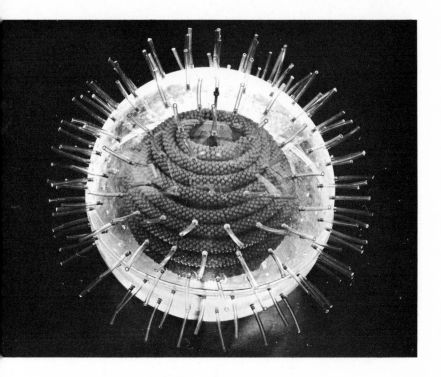

PLATE 7. Model constructed to show the relationship of the inner helical component to the outer envelope in the myxoviruses. Photograph by R. W. Horne, A. P. Waterson, P. Wildy, and A. E. Farnham, *Virology*, 1961, Academic Press Inc.

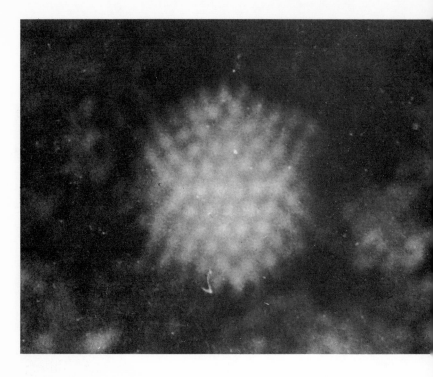

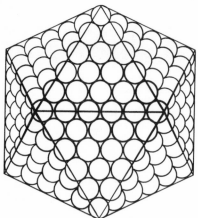

PLATE 8. A particle of human adenovirus showing the icosahedral symmetry of the protein shell. The drawing shows the geometric arrangement of the particle's 252 surface subunits, or capsomeres. Photograph by R. W. Horne, S. Brenner, A. P. Waterson, and P. Wildy, *Journal of Molecular Biology*, 1959, Academic Press Inc. Drawing from a drawing in *Scientific American*.

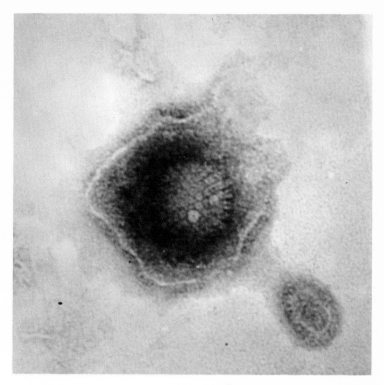

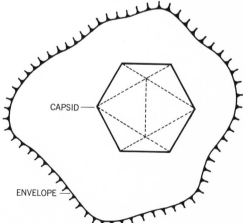

CAPSID

ENVELOPE

PLATE 9. Herpes simplex virus showing the protein coat, or capsid, enclosed in the outer envelope. The capsid contains 162 hollow capsomeres, each of which is composed of six smaller structure units. Photograph by P. Wildy, W. Russell, and R. W. Horne, *Virology*, 1960, Academic Press Inc.

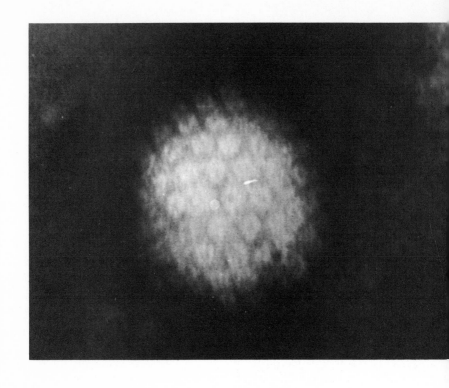

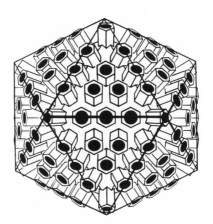

PLATE 10. In this electron micrograph, the outer envelope of the herpes virus particle has been removed and the icosahedral capsid can be seen. Photograph by P. Wildy, W. Russell, and R. W. Horne, *Virology*, 1960, Academic Press Inc. Drawing after a drawing in *Scientific American*.

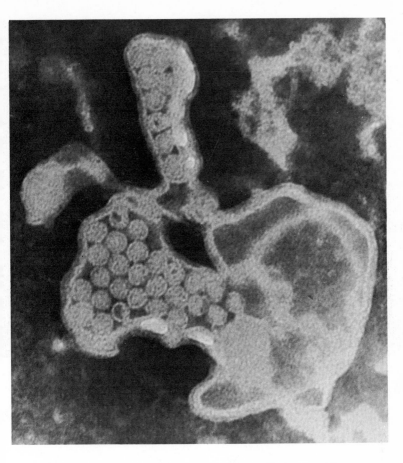

PLATE 11. Tissue culture fragment showing poliovirus particles arrayed in the cytoplasm of a human cell. Photograph by R. W. Horne and J. Nagington, *Journal of Molecular Biology*, 1959, Academic Press Inc.

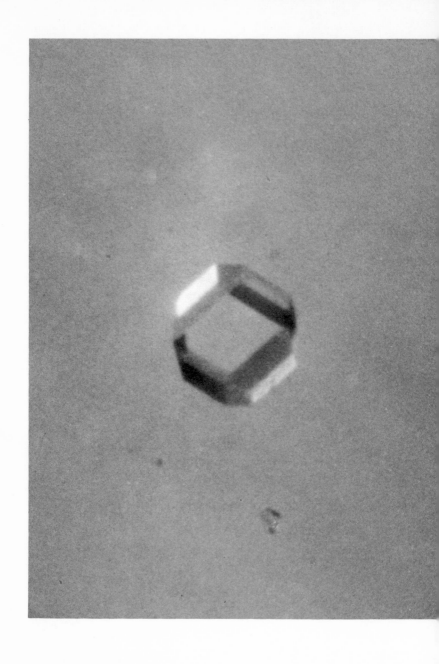

PLATE 12. Large octahedral crystal of poliovirus, the first human virus to be obtained in crystalline form. Photograph by Russell L. Steere and F. L. Schaffer, *Biochimica and Biophysica*, 1958.

later work on polio, recalls that one of the experts of the 1930s stated wearily, after attempting to study the spread of the disease, that he could only conclude that the safest place to be during a polio epidemic was in bed with a polio victim. Compounding the problem was the fact that it was not unknown for a person who had had one attack of paralytic disease to suffer a second one; this happened rarely, but the disease itself was a rare one.

In the second place, and probably most important, the techniques were not available. The work was difficult and expensive and the only animals known to be susceptible to the disease were monkeys, which were hard to obtain and extremely expensive. With bacteriophage, for instance, an experiment could be repeated over and over again until the last ambiguity could be explored and eliminated. In polio, experiments were kept at a level permitting scarcely more than "impressions," as investigators of those days freely admit, and it is scant wonder that many of these impressions turned out to be wrong.

Differences between man and the bad-tempered, unfortunate rhesus monkey that served as his stand-in compounded the confusion. When monkeys were infected with the virus, which was given to them in a filtered suspension of mashed-up spinal cord from a fatal case of the disease, they nearly always developed a severe paralysis and often died; in fact, to insure such "takes," the virus was usually inoculated right into the brains of the animals. If the filtrate did not produce these effects, the experiment was not considered successful or the disease was not considered polio. Under these circumstances, it was easy to overlook the most salient fact about poliomyelitis, which is that it is a widely prevalent intestinal infection that only rarely infects nervous tissue and, indeed, seldom causes any remarkable symptoms whatsoever.

Despite this appalling ignorance of the disease, two polio vaccines were given public trials in 1934 and 1935,

one made from a live attenuated virus and one from virus
killed with formaldehyde. Neither of these was either safe
or effective, but some 20,000 persons, mostly children,
were inoculated before the vaccines were withdrawn.
Twelve cases of paralytic disease, with six deaths, were
associated with the two vaccines, and following this experience, interest in experimental vaccines for poliomyelitis lapsed for many years.

After the vaccine fiasco, scientific attention was turned
to the problem of how polio spread from man to man.
Largely because of technical inadequacies, virus had not
been found in the blood streams of persons with obvious
disease or of the people with whom they had come into
contact. Polio was believed to grow only in nerve cells,
but since man obviously did not contract polio in the
normal course of events by having it injected into his
brain, it was necessary to explain how it reached the target cells. It was known by then that rabies, a truly neuro-
tropic virus, once it makes its way into the body through
the bite wound, travels up the nerve trunks to the brain,
with the incubation period of the disease being in direct
proportion to the distance of the bite from the brain.
One of the most popular postulates about polio was that
the virus was breathed in through the air and that it
gained access to the body by way of the olfactory nerve,
along which it could travel to the central nervous system. When monkeys were given polio virus by nasal inoculation, they developed the disease, and when their nasal
passages were painted in a "chemical blockade," the monkeys no longer contracted polio virus from the nasal inoculation. In retrospect, this would seem a rather closed
experimental system, but nevertheless in 1936 and 1937
the nasal passages of almost 10,000 children were sprayed
with zinc sulphate before both practice and theory were
simultaneously abandoned.

At the end of the 1930s there were three important
events in the history of polio, and the current shifted.

In 1939 Charles Armstrong of the United States Public Health Service adapted one strain of polio virus to grow in the cotton rat and in the mouse following intracerebral inoculation; at last a practical means was at hand for carrying the virus in the laboratory and making quantitative studies with it. The following year Howe and David Bodian of Johns Hopkins found that the chimpanzee is susceptible to poliomyelitis. The chimpanzee is no more convenient as a laboratory host than the rhesus monkey, but unlike the monkey, and like man, it is infected by the oral route, which provided a useful reorientation in the concept of the spread of polio.

At about this same time the National Foundation for Infantile Paralysis was founded, which, under the leadership of Basil O'Connor, carried out the most mammoth and successful fund-raising campaign in history. The bulk of the money went where it was desperately needed, for the treatment of patients, but the ten per cent or so that was allocated to research resulted directly in the Salk and the Sabin vaccines and also in a tremendous and vigorous growth of virology as a whole. The success of the Foundation's research investment program, which was guided largely by O'Connor's medical adviser, Thomas Rivers, was that it did not try to establish or direct specific programs of research, but rather, at the beginning, recognized that the need was for development of men to do the work and of the ideas that would make the work possible. Salk trained under a National Foundation fellowship, as did James Watson and hundreds of other investigators who, like Salk and Watson, may or may not have spent much of their time in programs that might be categorized as polio research. Robley Williams received Foundation support for electron microscopy studies, as did Enders' group, although Enders' chief and avowed interest was in mumps, and Pauling received support for studies of the basic structure of proteins. Thousands were spent in what have become known in modern parlance as seed grants, many of which bore no relationship to the development of polio vaccines, but, as Edward Tatum once put it, "O'Connor practically created virology," and also the Foundation program gave tremendous impetus to programs that might be considered as "related," such as molecular biology and cancer research.

During the 1940s the availability of March of Dimes money made possible the long-needed surveys for the presence of the polio virus. And it turned out that the virus was everywhere, in sewage, on the feet of house-flies, in the stools and intestines of healthy persons, in the urban sewers of cities from Toronto to Johannes-burg, and during months in which not a single case of paralytic polio had been reported. Then at last the true picture of the great human reservoir of poliomyelitis be-gan to emerge. The virus was ubiquitous. In primitive countries, mothers all have antibodies to polio viruses circulating in their blood streams. These pass to their unborn children through the placenta and, before this passive immunity is worn off completely, there is a good chance that the infant has been exposed to polio, had a mild case, and become actively immune. Almost all in-fants in Cairo, for example, one survey showed, have anti-bodies to the major types of polio by the time they are three years old. During these three years, if the infant manages to survive diarrhea, tuberculosis, and the other abounding infectious diseases, he is invulnerable to polio. But in the land of diaper service, the flush toilet, and the screened crib, the infant is far less likely to be exposed to the contents of anyone else's intestines until long after his maternally supplied antibodies, if any, have worn off and perhaps not until adulthood. Apparently also, the young adult is more likely to be paralyzed by polio than the infant or child. The reasons for this are not known, but they may be hormone-linked since it is well estab-lished that pregnancy greatly increases one's risks of con-tracting a severe infection with the virus. So, paradoxi-

cally, an infection of infancy, generally so mild as to go
unnoticed for centuries, became, in conditions of advanced sanitation, a crippling disease of children and
young adults.

In 1947 Isabel Mountain Morgan with Howe and Bodian
at Johns Hopkins showed conclusively, almost forty years
after Landsteiner's first experiments along the same line,
that monkeys which have survived a non-lethal infection
with one strain of polio are protected against reinocula-
tion even right into the brain with that same strain. In
1948 she reported that inoculation of monkeys with polio
virus which had been killed by formaldehyde also afforded
active protection against reinfection with that same
strain. The following year, Bodian, Morgan, and Howe
found that nineteen separately isolated polio viruses could
all fit into three immunological categories. The National
Foundation increased its fund-raising effort and that same
year launched a massive study to type 100 different polio
viruses.

That same year, in 1949, Enders' group, in a brief formal
report in *Science*, announced that polio could be grown
in "various human tissues" in tissue culture. This seemingly simple observation meant that polio research was
freed at last from the burden of the experimental animal.
Secondly, it provided the medium on which polio virus
could be safely cultivated for a human vaccine.

In 1951 the Committee on Typing finished its survey:
all 100 of the strains tested fitted into one of three immunologic groups. In other words, a triple, or "trivalent,"
vaccine could probably immunize against most polio viruses. That same year Jonas Salk, who had been a member
of the Typing Committee, began work at the University
of Pittsburgh on a formaldehyde-killed vaccine. Salk established that monkey kidney cells were the most practical material on which to cultivate large amounts of the
virus and that in such cultures the virus could be harvested easily from the fluid bathing the cells. He selected

the three representative strains of virus and worked out the amount of formaldehyde and the length of exposure necessary to "inactivate" the virus without destroying its ability to produce antibodies. Salk himself vaccinated some 12,000 persons in 1952 and 1953, including himself and his three young sons. In 1954 a massive field trial was initiated under the direction of Thomas Francis, Jr., of the University of Michigan. This trial involved some two million children, of whom 423,000 received three doses of the vaccine, 200,000 received placebo injections, and the others were kept under observation as controls. In April 1955, over a coast-to-coast closed television network Francis announced to physicians assembled in movie theaters that the vaccine had been sixty to ninety per cent effective in protecting vaccinated children (depending on the strain to which they were exposed), and that it was safe. That same day the vaccine was licensed for commercial production.

Almost from that moment of triumph on, the course was downhill. In the early period of enthusiasm and excitement following the announcement, insufficient vaccine was available for everyone to be inoculated, and rumors of physicians peddling vaccine, allocated to first and second graders, to their adult patients somewhat dimmed the new luster of the medical profession. Worse still, within a matter of days after the Francis report, news began to come in that children inoculated with the vaccine were coming down with polio. At first it seemed a coincidence, but five children from California all developed polio first in their left arms, where they had received the injections, and all who recalled the vaccine disaster of twenty years before recognized this grim omen. During the weeks that followed there were 204 cases of polio and eleven deaths resulting from the vaccine, some caused by direct inoculation and others by secondary infection from persons who had been vaccinated. Apparently a preparation had been released from one of the commercial laboratories in which some of the particles of one strain were still infectious, and these particles had not shown up in the checking tests. There remains some question as to whether this tragic incident would have occurred if the Foundation's work and Francis' announcement had been carried out with less fanfare; it seems that it probably would not, since all of the laboratories licensed to produce the vaccine, as they later admitted, were having difficulty with the inactivation procedure and had been forced to discard many batches that were found to have live virus during the required preliminary assay in monkeys. In a less excited atmosphere, time might have been taken to solve these problems of commercial production before the country was flooded with vaccines. In 1956, 8000 cases of polio were reported and in 1957 the total fell to 2500, only fifty per cent of the average of the five preceding years. But somehow there is no way to write off those eleven deaths on the balance books.

Once the sound of trumpets had faded away, commercial production methods had been revised, and a safe vaccine was at last in ample supply, the forces of medical progress encountered a totally unexpected roadblock: people simply would not bother to go to doctors or clinics for the series of necessary injections. In 1959 there were more than 6000 cases of polio in the country, nearly all among the unvaccinated, and an estimated forty million persons still needing vaccination.

By this time, clinical trials were well under way on an oral vaccine. This work was started in the early fifties, chiefly by Harold Cox and Hilary Koprowski at the Lederle Laboratories and by Albert Sabin of the University of Cincinnati. The principle was simply to attenuate the virus by growing it in a medium other than human nerve tissue; in the course of such culture, mutations occur in the virus, as they would have in its natural host, but, in the artificial medium, mutations favoring neurotropism are at a selective disadvantage, so the strain becomes less and less

virulent. Small-scale clinical trials were carried out by
Koprowski as early as 1952, using a strain of virus that
had been carried in the cotton rat, but the authorities
were long hesitant about permitting widespread use of
an oral vaccine in this country. Too many tragedies had
occurred with the other polio vaccines and live virus presented new problems that were difficult to evaluate. A
child who had received the live vaccine could spread it to
his playmates, and as it spread from child to child might
it not revert to its old and evil ways? At one point it was
suggested that everyone in the world, on awakening on
one specific morning, swallow a dose of oral vaccine, but
this probably could not have been organized even by the
National Foundation.

On the other hand, oral vaccine has several clear advantages. The first is ease of administration; it is obviously
simpler to persuade either child or adult to eat a piece of
candy than to be stuck with a needle. Second, it is
cheaper; very little virus is required to initiate the infection and very little medical manpower is required to ad-
minister the program. Third, because the virus spreads
itself, the vaccinated immunize the unvaccinated, and
fourth, for reasons that are not clearly understood, the
oral vaccine seems to create immunity in the intestinal
tract as well as in the blood stream; thus the individual
who has been immunized by the attenuated polio virus not
only is protected against paralytic disease but cannot
carry the virus and so eventually the agent, homeless,
will entirely disappear, like yellow fever which was driven
out by the elimination of the mosquito. By the late 1950s
Sabin had developed attenuated strains that appeared
both safe and stable and with them began widespread
clinical trials in Russia, vaccinating millions of persons,
and the oral vaccine has now been used in many countries, including the United States. In 1963 there were only
500 cases of polio reported in the United States, and in
some areas of the world, where the Sabin vaccine has been

intensively distributed, polio seems to have disappeared completely.

One might think that this victory of medical science would chart a clear course for immunizing everyone against everything, at least against all virus diseases, but actually the polio vaccines may represent the last of the great successes of vaccination in the strictly Jennerian sense. Some viruses do not seem amenable to such manipulation. A case in point is influenza, which derives its name from the Italian word for "influence," although whether the influence referred to is of the cold, the stars, the noxious airs, or some divinity is not entirely clear. Influenza is certainly the most serious of the remaining known virus diseases; polio, while greatly feared, was never a major cause of death, while the flu, which has always been treated lightly, is the most wanton killer of all. The 1918–19 epidemic of "Spanish influenza" was the worst of the great plagues of history. In October 1918, 400,000 Americans died of flu or its sequelae, and the following winter 500 million persons—"half the world"— contracted the disease, and twenty-one million died of it. The panglobal epidemic of "Asian flu" of 1957–58 was equally virulent, but by that time antibiotics had been developed to control the bacterial pneumonia that so often followed in its wake, and so, although morbidity was high, in this country at least, only the old and infirm or the very young died.

Some of the best virologists of modern times have bent their lances on the influenza problem. The virus was isolated more than thirty years ago and can be grown readily in the fertilized egg. It is a good antibody producer and in fact, vaccines for influenza, effective in the laboratory, have been available for some twenty years. The problem is that the virus, in nature's most remarkable display of evolutionary prowess, always manages to outflank the immune defenses of the public. Burnet, who has studied the virus intensively, has been able to show that under laboratory conditions, at least, two different influenza viruses will recombine, just as two types of phage can recombine, to make a third type, and he credits the remarkable mutability of the disease at least in part to this phenomenon. In any case, it is clear that antibodies against last year's influenza are hopelessly out of date by the next year. In a small community, the disease spreads like wildfire, since the incubation period is only twenty-four to forty-eight hours. In a world-wide epidemic, which may be making its way from one hemisphere to another, it may be possible to prepare vaccines far enough in advance to protect at least the most susceptible portions of the population, but only very temporarily.

The most recent of the new vaccines, at this writing, is that developed against measles. In this country, measles is considered an inconsequential childhood disease, but again this is largely because its ugly aftereffects can generally be controlled by antibiotics, although it still may leave deafness or mental crippling in its wake. In some parts of South America and Africa, the death rate among children from measles may run as high as twenty-five per cent; in Chile, for instance, measles accounts for half the deaths from communicable disease. Furthermore, it is the most contagious of all the virus diseases, with only about one per cent escaping infection after exposure. Measles vaccine is clearly effective, but the problem is that it is also expensive, so that its cost may be prohibitive for its use in just those areas of the world and among those populations that need it the most.

The measles story serves to illustrate that the development of new vaccines may be reaching the point of diminishing returns. For example, scientists and laymen alike have talked long and hopefully about "licking the common cold," and it has usually been assumed that this will be accomplished by a "shot," but dozens of viruses have now been shown to induce that all too familiar syndrome and so a vaccine, while not impossible, would undoubtedly be expensive. Also, since cold viruses, like those of influenza, multiply primarily in the respiratory tract in the first cells they encounter, a very high level of antibodies must be present in the blood to spill over into these peripheral tissues, so that repeated immunizations might well be required. Under these circumstances, when one considers the problems of promoting mass immunizations against the dreaded infantile paralysis, it seems likely that a cold vaccine, although joyously heralded, would not be widely used. Similarly, although intensive efforts are under way to grow the viruses of hepatitis and German measles in the laboratory, one wonders if a large proportion of the population would not simply choose to run the risks.

10   The Barriers

Over the evolutionary millenniums, living organisms have devised many means for their self-preservation. Some of these—the porcupine's quills, the rhinoceros' hide, the shield of the armadillo—are obvious and formidable. Others are less conspicuous: the tiny hairs, cilia, that brush foreign objects from the respiratory tract; the bacteria-killing enzyme, lysozyme, in tears, saliva, and other body fluids; and chemicals that seep through the pores. Even man's naked and seemingly vulnerable skin thus becomes an effective barrier, at least to the microbial world.

If a micro-organism, or indeed any foreign particle, succeeds in penetrating these outer walls, it is confronted by a complex internal defense system. Injury to a body cell triggers the release of histamine and other chemicals which lead to inflammation. The tiny blood vessels in the area become distended and more permeable. Circulating white blood cells seep through the distended capillaries and concentrate at the site of the injury. One type of white cell, the phagocytes, engulf foreign particles in a primitive "eat or be eaten response" which, as Elie Metchnikoff, the tempestuous Russian, remarked 100 years ago, we share with the amoeba. Other white cells wall off the affected area. Local temperature and acidity may rise, creating an environment unfavorable to the multiplication of the micro-organism while accelerating the motion of the phagocytes. A vast network of fixed cells in the lymphatic tissue, the liver, the spleen, and the lining of the blood vessels—all of which make up the reticulo-endothelial system—also possess phagocytic capacities. In addition, there are chemicals in the blood that appear to act upon certain types of pathogens. Most bacteria do not get past these defenses.

Antibodies

Within a few days or weeks following the entry of a new substance into the blood stream, antibodies to that substance appear. Antibodies are protein molecules, each composed of a chain or chains of hundreds of amino acids. In the 1930s, in Sweden, Arne Tiselius demonstrated that the proteins in the blood can be divided into four groups on the basis of their electrical charges (just as Pauling, some years later, separated hemoglobins by the same criteria); these four groups are albumin, which is composed of smaller molecules, and alpha, beta, and gamma globulin. The gamma globulins all seem to be antibodies, but since most of the substances against which antibodies have been produced—splinters, pollen, bits of dust, hordes of harmless bacteria, fungi, protozoa, viruses, orphan and otherwise—are unidentifiable it is difficult to prove that every gamma globulin molecule is an antibody against something.

As Paul Ehrlich first postulated, just before the turn of the century, antibodies and antigens fit together in a chemical union. Although both are typically large molecules, the active or combining sites are small, making up only about one per cent of the surface of the molecule and involving only some ten or twenty of the amino acids. The amino acids in the active site, it is believed, are not adjacent to one another along the peptide chain but are brought together by the intricate convolutions of the molecule as it assumes its three-dimensional shape. Each antibody seems to have two or three such active sites which are visualized as small pockets into which particular parts of the antigen fit, like a key into a lock. Because this reaction is so highly specific, antibodies can be put to a great variety of laboratory uses, in the crime laboratory, for instance, where, as any reader of detective stories knows, they can reveal whether a drop of blood is that of the victim, the newsboy, or last night's joint of beef, or in biochemistry, in which they are used to distinguish closely related, complex organic molecules, such as enzymes, from one another. Rabbits are usually employed as antibody producers, since they are of convenient size and habits for maintaining in the laboratory and blood samples can be taken readily from the large blood vessels in their ears.

A micro-organism or a bit of living tissue evokes a whole spectrum of antibodies. In the case of viruses, two strains may induce identical antibodies; others, like smallpox and vaccinia, are not identical but share many antibodies, and so immunity to one provides immunity to the other. Influenza A, on the other hand, shares a common antigen by which all the strains can be classified as belonging to A, rather than B, C, or D, each of which similarly shares a common antigen, but this is useful in the laboratory and helps not at all in questions of natural defense.

There is at present under vigorous debate a number of questions about the way in which antibodies are formed, their extraordinary specificity, and their remarkable memory. In the 1930s it was postulated that the antigen, or some part of it, persists in the antibody-forming cells and forms a template against which the antibody molecules are struck off. In the 1950s Burnet, who received the Nobel Prize in 1960 for his work in this field, proposed in a more Darwinian theory that the body innately possesses cells capable of producing all possible antibodies and that the function of the antigen is to select the particular cell or cells that can make antibodies against it and to trigger its activity and multiplication. This is known as the "clonal selection theory." The future will decide between them, or, as is even more likely on the basis of history, propose a third.

Self and Not Self

Another question which has attracted much recent attention has been the means by which the body decides what is foreign and what is not. How can a rabbit tell his own enzyme from the very similar enzyme of another animal and so form antibodies against the second but not the first? Or how can the burnt child recognize the skin graft from his brother as being alien and so, no matter how desperately he needs the protective tissue, reject it, unless the brother is also his identical twin? Similarly, only animals of the same extremely inbred strain—all of which, genetically speaking, are also essentially identical twins—can exchange tissues with one another.

Twin cattle, even if not identical twins, sometimes share the same placenta and so the same blood supply. This has long been recognized as the cause of the free-martin, the heifer sterilized by male hormones supplied *in utero* by her twin brother. In 1945 Ray Owen of the University of Wisconsin observed that such a twin calf may have two types of blood cells, one its own and the other its twin's. Such animals, he found, that have exchanged blood-borne cells in fetal life can exchange other tissues throughout their lifetimes. Working from this clue, it was found that the ability to form antibodies does not develop until fairly late in embryonic life—the exact time depends on the species of animal and also, new evidence indicates, on the nature of the antigen. Any possible antigen that is present during this critical period when the organism decides what is "self" and what is "not self," as Burnet puts it, is thereafter accepted, and production of antibodies against it is "forbidden."

There are some exceptions. The lens of the eye and parts of the central nervous system are isolated from the general circulation and so their antigens do not ordinarily come into contact with antibody-forming cells. This is why injury to one eye, which may cause lens protein to leak into the general circulation, may result in the formation of antibodies that may harm the other eye. If a portion of an animal's brain is removed and injected into its blood stream, immune responses to this brain tissue can cause brain damage. Apparently by a similar mechanism, nervous tissue from other animals can evoke "anti-brain" antibodies or other immune responses that cause the "allergic encephalitis" seen in about one in 1000 persons who receive rabies vaccine, grown in rabbit spinal cord.

Also, from time to time, there is apparently a slip-up in the recognition system and antibodies are formed against the organism's own tissues. When the tissue under attack is a vital one, such as the kidney, such auto-immune diseases, as they are called, can be fatal.

Immunologic tolerance can be acquired to viruses as to any other antigen present in early life. As long ago as 1935, Erich Traub of The Rockefeller Institute was surprised to find that lymphocytic choriomeningitis, a virus disease, was endemic in his colony of laboratory mice. They had no symptoms of it and no antibodies against it, but when fresh mice were introduced into the colony, the newcomers all developed the disease, with symptoms and antibodies. He found that the mice had all acquired the infection before birth. It has been hypothesized that this disease is really more an auto-immune disease than a virus disease, with the symptoms resulting primarily from immune responses to the virus-infected cells.

Cortisone and the cortisone-like hormones produced by the adrenal cortex can modify these immune responses. This is probably why these hormones are effective in a wide spectrum of diseases ranging from poison ivy to inflammatory arthritis, in which the symptoms are due primarily to the host's reactions. Similarly, because cortisone depresses the immune responses, a disease as mild as chicken pox may be lethal in a patient under cortisone treatment. Further, since cortisone is produced by the adrenal in response to stress, this may explain why chills, fatigues, and emotional upsets—all of which increase cortisone production—can precipitate colds and other virus infections, as Adelaide lamented in *Guys and Dolls*.

Antibodies play an important role in the recovery from bacterial disease. In pneumonia caused by the pneumococcus, which is probably the most studied of all infections from the immunological point of view, there is a point some ten days after the onset of the disease at which the "crisis" occurs. If this is weathered successfully, the fever and delirium subside, the patient usually falls into a restful sleep, and the process of recovery begins. The crisis, it has been shown, is that point at which antibody production catches up with bacterial multiplication. The bacteria, thus neutralized, are gathered up by the phagocytes and hustled out of the body. Before the days of antibiotics, if this did not occur, the patient died.

A few months later, if another pneumococcus of the same strain seeks entry to that same organism, the antibody response is immediate and overwhelming, reaching within a matter of hours a higher level than its peak at the "crisis." This "secondary response" routs the invader before it can set up any sort of active infection.

The length of time that an organism "remembers" an invader seems to vary with the antigen. We seem to recall the pneumococcus for only about six months; after that there is no overwhelming secondary response and new infection is possible. The memory of viruses persists for a remarkably long time however. With many of them, smallpox, mumps, measles, yellow fever, one attack usually immunizes for a lifetime, even though there seems to have been no subsequent exposure to the agent. Roger Herriot of Johns Hopkins has suggested that this may come about because just enough viral nucleic acid remains in eclipse in some of the infected cells to produce an occasional small burst of virus particles that jog the immunological memory, like a "booster" shot. Use of a killed-virus preparation, such as the Salk vaccine, for immunizing purposes was criticized because it was assumed that immunity would be of much shorter duration than that produced by a vaccine made of an attenuated virus, but actually the protection has been surprisingly persistent.

Antibodies can be transferred from one person to another and will provide some transient immunity. In nature they pass through the placenta to the fetus from the maternal blood stream, and so the newborn child is protected for the first few weeks of life against those diseases to which his mother is immune. Pooled gamma globulin, or "anti-sera," taken from blood samples of persons who have been exposed to a particular disease may be used to protect persons following a known exposure or to ameliorate the effects of a disease. Passive immunity, as this is called, lasts only a few weeks.

Viral Interference

In 1952 Colonel Ogden Bruton of the Walter Reed Army Hospital, in the course of his medical practice, came across a young boy who had had eighteen severe infections within four years and who had no gamma globulin. By 1956, sixty-six additional similar cases were reported, none of whom had any signs of antibodies circulating in their blood streams. Bacterial diseases in these patients were very severe, but they could be pulled through by the use of antibiotics. On the other hand, recovery from viral infections appeared to be perfectly normal.

This finding helped to bring into focus the restive feelings of a number of investigators who were harboring the opinion that antibodies, although strong allies against the bacteria, may have received too much credit for their role in recovery from virus infections. As a result, there has been a quickening interest in other components of the defense system which may be involved in resistance to virus infections and which could thus possibly be manipulated, as the antibody-forming system has been successfully manipulated from the time of Jenner, to aid in the recovery from disease.

A phenomenon that had attracted attention from time to time was that of viral interference. Jenner in 1804 had remarked that herpes infection might prevent successful vaccination. In 1937 Dalldorf found that if monkeys were infected with lymphocytic choriomeningitis, they failed to become paralyzed when superinfected with polio, and the spinal cords of the double-infected monkeys did not contain as much virus as those that had been infected with polio alone. The two viruses were, as Dalldorf noted, antigenically totally unrelated. This observation was subsequently confirmed with various other virus combinations. This protective effect of one virus against another lasted about two weeks.

In the 1940s when viral interference, as it came to be called, was re-examined in tissue culture, it was found that it occurred in the test tube as well, pin-pointing the event at the cellular level. It was then generally assumed that two viruses or viral components competed for the same location within the cell, with the first arrival accorded squatter's rights. In 1943 Gertrude and Warner Henle of the Children's Hospital of Philadelphia showed that inoculation of chick embryo cells in tissue culture with influenza virus that had been inactivated by heat or by irradiation protected the cells from superinfection by influenza virus. This was the first clue that viruses might interfere with themselves as well as with viruses of other strains.

In the late 1950s, Alex Isaacs of the National Institute for Medical Research in London, with Jean Lindenmann of his laboratory, was studying viral interference, using the Henles' system. They incubated chick embryo tissue with heat-killed influenza virus and then took a second step, which actually could have been taken a quarter of a century before. They removed the chick embryo cells and the virus particles from the test tube and then added fresh, non-infected tissue to the same medium. This tissue was also resistant to infection by viruses. The test tube contained something that had been elaborated by the cell into the surrounding extracellular fluid and which blocked the viral multiplication in other cells. Isaacs called this something "interferon."

Since Isaacs' discovery, his observations have been repeated, confirmed, and extended by scores of experiments. Every type of virus tried—large, small, active, inactive, DNA, RNA, adeno-, entero-, myxo-, or pox—has been shown to produce interferon in any tissue that supports its growth, although there are wide variations in the quantity produced. Also, as Monte Ho at the University of Pittsburgh has emphasized, this inhibition is not an all-or-nothing phenomenon, but can occur in varying degrees and can be overcome by large inocula of virus. The interferon, in turn, will protect the cell type that produced it against almost any sort of virus and also will protect other cells growing with it in mixed cultures. Curiously, although interferon is a fairly large protein molecule, it does not seem to evoke immune responses in another species. Interferon produced by one species has less effect and sometimes no effect in other species, however, so it is considered better form to refer to the interferons.

Ho showed that chick embryo cells that have been treated with interferon are resistant to the infectious RNA from polio virus, showing that interferon does not affect any of the various mechanisms involved in viral penetration or shedding of the protein coat, but acts during the so-called eclipse phase of the virus cycle. More recently, Isaacs has shown that any "foreign" nucleic acid, whether viral or not, can stimulate the production of interferon, or that even the nucleic acid that has been extracted from an identical cell and in which small mutations have been produced by chemicals can stimulate interferon production. He suggests that interferon may have evolved not just as a defense against viruses but against all false genetic messengers that are "not self," as a way by which an organism can preserve its genetic integrity. Like antibody production, the ability to produce interferon is acquired in the course of embryonic life.

The extent of the role that interferon plays in natural recovery from virus infection is not clear. Chick embryos, which cannot produce antibodies at all, may recover from virus infections after the eighth day of life, which is the time when interferon production begins. Influenza in man lasts only two or three days and then subsides, although antibodies reach significant levels only well after virus multiplication has subsided. In localities where intestinal infections are endemic, the live-virus polio vaccine may not "take" and, as a consequence, authorities in these countries advise oral inoculation in winter months, when concurrent intestinal infections are less likely to be encountered. Similarly Sabin has found that multiplication of one attenuated strain of polio may interfere with that of another, and so advises giving each separately. In short, growing clinical evidence indicates that interferon is an important component of the immunological system.

One hope is, of course, that interferon might prove useful in treating virus infections. It would have many advantages as a therapeutic agent. It works against a large virus spectrum, it is not toxic, and it has little or no antigenicity, so it could be given in large amounts, over and over again. In Great Britain the government has taken an active interest in the question of its usefulness in man. Under the aegis of the National Medical Research Council, a group of volunteers were vaccinated against smallpox at two sites, one of which had been treated previously with interferon. In more than half the group, the vaccinations took only at the untreated site. Similarly, interferon has proved effective in the control of some accidental vaccinia infections in the eye. In mice it shows some activity in generalized viral infections if it can be maintained at high levels. A chief problem is to obtain adequate supplies for testing and for use. As Isaacs has stated, the soundest of approaches may be to learn to stimulate the natural production of interferon and so enhance its protective effects.

The other hope is, of course, that as more is learned about interferon, more will be learned perforce of the way in which cells can recognize foreign nucleic acids and act against them and also perhaps something of the role of these genetic messengers in the growth and differentiation of living things.

11   The Cancer Viruses II

Many physicians have been struck by the resemblance of the leukemias to infectious diseases. Leukemic patients are systemically ill, they have spontaneous improvements and relapses, have swollen glands, run fevers, and sometimes even develop rashes and itching. If any kinds of cancer are caused by viruses, investigators reasoned, it must be these, and the failure to isolate a mammalian leukemia virus, despite many sporadic attempts, served to darken the cloud that hung over the entire virus cancer field.

Ludwik Gross began to work on the problem in 1945. At that time he was still on duty with the U. S. Army Medical Corps, a former storage room for oxygen tanks in the basement of the Veterans' Hospital in the Bronx serving as his laboratory. There was no shortage of mouse leukemia for study. Strains of animals had been developed such as the Ak strain, in which leukemia develops spontaneously in ninety per cent of the adult animals. In other strains, however, such as the C3H, less than one half of one per cent of the animals come down with the disease. Even in the lower cancer strains, leukemia can be induced by a number of chemicals and by whole body irradiation. Also, it can be readily transferred from one animal to another of the same strain by injections of whole blood or cell suspensions of a leukemic organ such as the spleen; in such cases the disease develops in about two weeks.

The high leukemia strain animals would be the most likely sources of a virus, Gross decided, and one could demonstrate it most convincingly in the low leukemia strain. He prepared cell-free filtrates from the leukemia cells of Ak mice and injected them into C3H animals over and over again for years with no results. In retrospect, the reasons for the difficulty are easy to see. Mice have to be injected when they are only a few hours old; even a few days is too late. Gross was using the wrong type of filter, one which for perverse and unforeseeable reasons tended to adsorb these particular virus particles. There is a long latent period, many times longer than the two weeks it requires for a full-blown leukemia to appear after the inoculation of malignant cells. Even today with standardized techniques it is often not possible to recover virus from a spontaneous leukemia. And Bittner's findings with "the milk agent" were not paid sufficient heed, perhaps because this agent, although it was clearly a factor in the development of mouse mammary cancer, was not yet fully accepted as a virus.

By 1949 Gross was almost ready to abandon the project when Gilbert Dalldorf, then of the New York State Department of Health in Albany, reported that he could transmit a newly discovered virus—the Coxsackie virus—to mice, but only when they were newborn. Gross decided to give it one more try, using very young animals. This time he hit the right combination. Active virus made its way through the filter and was injected into newborn mice of the low leukemia strain. Within four to nine months, twenty-eight per cent of the animals developed leukemia.

Gross's first reports, in 1951, of his long and patient work in the Bronx basement were greeted by the same chorus of skepticism and implications of technical incompetence that have welcomed similar major discoveries in the cancer virus field. In addition to the technical difficulties of the work, there were added complications owing to variations in the strains of mice in various laboratories where attempts were made to duplicate Gross's findings. Eventually, however, other experimenters were able to produce the same results and soon Gross obtained a more virulent inoculum which induced leukemia in up to ninety-eight per cent of the low leukemia strain mice, and his findings were finally accepted.

It seemed clear then that mice of the high leukemia strain harbored a virus that was passed from parent to offspring, probably through egg and sperm. Leukemia sometimes occurred in the low cancer strain, too, for example, following exposure to total body irradiation. Gross irradiated a group of C3H mice with 150 roentgens a week, once a week for four to six weeks. Seven to nine months later, about half developed leukemia. When cell-free filtrates of the leukemic organs were injected into newborn C3H animals, eleven per cent developed leukemia within the year. Apparently low leukemia strain mice also harbor a virus, but it almost never expresses itself under normal conditions. A few years before, it had been shown that irradiation can release a lysogenic bacteriophage, and many were struck by the coincidence.

Gross's work greatly stimulated the search for new cancer-causing viruses and, just as many runners seem to be able to run the four-minute mile once Roger Bannister showed the way, virus after virus has turned up in the last decade. Graffi of the German Academy of Sciences prepared filtrates from a large number of different types of transplanted mouse tumors and injected them into newborn mice. None of the animals developed tumors that in any way resembled those used for the preparation of the extracts but, curiously, a large number of them developed leukemia, most often of a type called chloroleukemia, because of the characteristic green discoloration of the lymph nodes that it causes.

At about the same time that Graffi began his work, Charlotte Friend at the Sloan-Kettering Institute in New York City was attempting to find a virus in the Ehrlich ascites tumor of mice, a common transplantable cancer in which the tumor cells grow in fluid in the peritoneal cavity, where the digestive organs are located. These cells offered special advantages for microscopic study since they can be readily separated from one another and spread out, ultrathin, for examination of their internal structure. In the course of such a study by the electron microscope it was observed that some of the tumor cells contained in their cytoplasm groups of round, regularly shaped particles, not unlike the particles seen in association with known viral diseases. Some forty times Friend prepared cell-free filtrates of the Ehrlich ascites carcinoma and injected them into newborn mice. Finally, in the experiment which she reported in 1956, she injected the filtrates into thirty newborns which, her interest in the project waning, she left practically unobserved for most of their lifetimes. After fourteen months of waiting, she sacrificed the animals, all of which were in apparently perfect health, and performed careful autopsies on every one of them. No trace of tumor was found, but in six of the thirty the spleens were somewhat enlarged. Still on the dimming trail of a virus, Friend removed the spleens from the six animals, minced them, and transplanted the cells into six separate groups (one for each spleen) of five mice each. This time no newborn animals were on hand, so the new recipients were all adults. No cancer or any other abnormality appeared in the mice of four of the six groups, but three mice of the fifth group and three mice of the sixth group developed enlarged spleens. These tissues were again removed and inoculated into fresh mice. This time a majority of them developed similar symptoms.

All passages since the first were made with minced tissue, not cell-free filtrates. Friend had no wish to risk losing whatever it was she had by trying to filter it; even well-established virus strains have been known to vanish completely in the course of ordinary, routine experiments.

At this stage, however, she took the risk and prepared cell-free filtrates from half of the material. Also, in this same experiment, instead of sacrificing the animals as soon as the enlarged spleen was palpable, she let them live on to study what happened next. She found first that as many of the filtrate-inoculated animals developed large spleens as did the cell-inoculated animals and, second, that as the animals grew older they developed not Ehrlich carcinoma but leukemia.

The point of particular interest about this leukemia virus was that, unlike that of Gross, it was effective in adult mice. It produced that characteristic enlargement of the spleen in two or three days and a full-blown leukemia in about two weeks. Friend was able to make a vaccine against the leukemia, using formalin-killed cells to stimulate the antibody response, and to demonstrate that the vaccine could protect mice against infection.

In 1960 John B. Moloney at the National Cancer Institute recovered a highly active leukemia virus from another common laboratory tumor, Sarcoma 37. Graffi had also tried to get a virus from Sarcoma 37, but in his experiments only a small percentage of the mice developed leukemia, and, furthermore, the leukemia which had developed was different in many characteristics from that in Moloney's. It is now generally agreed that Graffi and Friend and Moloney in their experiments did not isolate the viruses that caused the tumors with which they were working, but that each found in these tumor cells a latent leukemia virus which was carried in the tumor tissues as an incidental companion. Some eight or ten more or less distinct mouse leukemia viruses are now known; it has been suggested that these form a family of related agents, like the chicken tumor viruses.

One of the most curious and controversial of the agents isolated during this period was that described by Steven O. Schwartz and his coworkers at the Cook County Hospital in Chicago. They first reported in 1956 that the development of spontaneous leukemia in mice of the high leukemia Ak strain could be substantially accelerated by inoculating "young adult" Ak mice with filtrates prepared from the brains of leukemic Ak mice. Moreover, and this is what attracted the most attention, filtrates prepared from the brains of human patients who had died of leukemia had a similar effect. In a continuation of this study, they reported in 1957 that filtrates from the brains of leukemic Swiss mice—a strain with a relatively low incidence of leukemia—could induce leukemia in a substantial portion of healthy young Swiss mice. The disease appeared after a short incubation period of only one to three weeks. The filtrates are leukemogenic only when they are prepared from the brains. Filtrates produced from leukemic tumors of the same animals failed to induce leukemia when inoculated under the same conditions.

Polyoma

Another seeker for leukemia virus during this fertile epoch was Sarah Stewart of the National Cancer Institute. As a point of departure, she attempted to repeat Gross's experiments. He had found, as he reported in 1953, that occasional mice injected with cell-free filtrates developed not leukemias but tumors of the parotid, the salivary gland in the neck that, in man, is affected by mumps. Stewart discovered that her filtrate produced no leukemias at all in the C3H animals of the strain she was using—although the same filtrate produced leukemia in another, hybrid strain—but only an occasional parotid tumor.

Stewart made cell-free filtrates of the parotid tumors and injected them into newborn C3H mice, but no tumors occurred. Interested in obtaining a more concentrated form of the virus, Stewart enlisted the help of Bernice Eddy, also of the National Institutes of Health, who had an elaborate tissue-culture laboratory. Stewart and Eddy discovered that by growing the virus in mouse embryo cells in the test tube, the factor that produced the parotid tumors became more virulent while that producing the leukemias disappeared. As a result of this work and of complementary work by Gross on the separation of the two agents, it became clear that the investigators were dealing with two viruses, Gross's leukemia virus and its frequent companion that caused the cancers of the parotid gland.

As the parotid tumor virus became more concentrated, cell-free filtrates from the tissue cultures produced tumors in eighty-five to 100 per cent of the animals to which they were administered, and not only parotid tumors but tumors of almost all of the glands of the head and neck, of the thymus, the mammary glands, the lungs and the adrenals—some twenty-six different types in all.

At first Stewart and Eddy could not believe that one virus could have such a great multiplicity of effects. Using methods developed with bacteriophage, they greatly diluted a sample of filtrate and spread it over a large colony of mouse embryo cells in tissue culture. As with the bacteriophages, a small focus of infection would appear at each spot where one virus particle began to multiply and the viruses collected from each spot were therefore known to be the progeny of a single particle. Each of these separate virus families was found to have all of the powers of the original cell-free filtrate.

Not only did the polyoma virus—as Stewart and Eddy called it—produce this multiplicity of tumors in a very unvirus-like way, but it readily infected almost any strain of laboratory mouse inoculated with it. The investigators tested it in other laboratory animals. In newborn rats it produced tumors, largely kidney sarcomas and subcutaneous tumors, in almost 100 per cent of the animals. The newborn hamster proved even more vulnerable to tumors than the mouse, with highly malignant cancers appearing only a week or two after injections.

The polyoma virus is a potent antibody inducer; this property both limits its effects and makes its trail easy to follow. As many as eighty per cent of mice in some colonies had antibodies to the virus, with the agent spreading, like many viruses, through saliva and feces. Animals in contact with infected animals frequently developed antibodies to the polyoma virus although they rarely developed tumors. Mothers passed antibodies to their newborn progeny through the milk. Laboratory workers who had handled the virus showed antibodies in their blood. Almost everywhere one looked, its tracks could be found.

Apparently Stewart and Eddy had not isolated a rare virus; they had come across one of the most common viruses of the laboratory mouse. In most animals the virus led a completely occult life, rarely causing the occurrence of a "spontaneous" tumor unless it found its way into an unusually susceptible host or into an environment such as the mouse embryo tissue culture provided for it, which favored its multiplication to unusually high levels.

In 1959 a group of scientists from Aaron Bendich's laboratory at the Sloan-Kettering Institute joined forces with Stewart and Eddy to study the nature of the infective and cancer-inducing component of polyoma virus.

The virus was inoculated into tissue cultures of mouse embryo cells. The viruses multiplied within the cells, producing characteristic cytopathic change and releasing new virus particles into the fluid. The virus-containing fluid was removed and the virus particles harvested from it. Then the protein coat was stripped off, leaving only the nucleic acid the particle had contained. When the isolated nucleic acid was added to a fresh culture of mouse embryo cells, it produced the same characteristic cytopathic effects as the whole virus particles. When the new virus particles—formed in the nucleic acid-infected cells —were inoculated into mice or hamsters, the disease produced was characteristic of that induced by polyoma virus. Finally, when the isolated nucleic acid itself was injected into laboratory animals, polyoma tumors were produced in a small but definite number of animals.

When the isolated nucleic acid was analyzed, it proved to be DNA, the first infective DNA to be found and also the first cancer-inducing nucleic acid, a combination which gave many cause to think. Perhaps after all it was true that cancer cells differed from normal cells, as the mutationists had believed for so long, simply by reason of a small difference in the hereditary DNA. And perhaps that small difference might be simply a single molecule of DNA, such as that slipped into the cell by the polyoma virus.

12   The Human Orphans

In the late 1940s Gilbert Dalldorf, like many other virologists at that time, was searching desperately for a host for polio other than the hard-to-get, expensive, rhesus monkey. In the summer of 1947 he collected fecal material from two young boys who apparently had mild cases of "infantile paralysis," as it was commonly called in those days, and began injecting filtrates of the material into possible laboratory hosts. Sporadic reports had recently appeared about the possibility of growing the virus in white mice, so these were among the animals that Dalldorf tested. In most of the mice, nothing happened, but some of the animals looked "odd," as Dalldorf now recalls, and a few of them even seemed to limp a little. Younger mice, he noticed, seemed more likely to show these effects than older ones.

Newborn mice are as small as the end of your finger, pink and hairless. It was generally agreed by laboratory investigators at that time that these baby mice were too delicate for any sort of manipulation and, besides, if they were handled, it was said their mothers would destroy them on their return to the maternal nest. Despite this cautionary consensus, Dalldorf's observations led him to experimenting with younger and younger animals until finally he began to inject sucklings and even newborns with samples of the filtrates. They did not die from the handling and they were not eaten by their mothers, but every one of them developed a highly characteristic acute paralytic infection. By this time Dalldorf knew that he was not working with polio—whatever the virus he had was, it would not grow in the rhesus monkey and was immunologically distinct from the known polio viruses—but the lid had been pried off Pandora's box and a host of new viruses were escaping.

The virus family that Dalldorf discovered came to be called the Coxsackie group; Coxsackie was the name of the town where the two sick children had been found; and, besides, there was no clear way to identify the agents. They cause a wide variety of fevers, aches, pains, muscle soreness, and intestinal upsets, usually of only a few days' duration—in fact, all of those symptoms which lead to the common public diagnosis, quite accurate as it turns out, of "having a little virus." Often they cause no disease at all; one in fifty children in almost any community at any given time harbors an active Coxsackie infection. Some thirty Coxsackie viruses now have been isolated, all distinct immunologically but identifiable as a group because of their highly characteristic effect in the newborn mouse.

Dalldorf first reported his results in 1948. Since that time an entire generation of virologists have lost countless hours of sleep at the bedsides of expectant laboratory mothers, and, as a result, have coaxed a number of new and sometimes surprising viruses out of hiding.

The ECHO Viruses

In the late 1940s, John Enders and his associates at Harvard found that a number of viruses could be made to grow in living cells growing in the test tube. In the course of these studies, Enders noticed what others had seen before but had not really grasped. When some of the viruses grew in the test-tube cultures, they caused visible cell damage, cytopathogenic effects, as they were known technically. These effects were a clear and simple indicator of the presence of the virus and also an index of the amount present and, in some instances, a clue to its nature. Instead of having to inject "something" into a laboratory host and wait, one could actually "see" the virus, or at least its traces. Virologists at last were able to stop working in the dark.

During the early 1950s, Enders' tissue-culture technique was widely used in the search for polio viruses, which was carried out on thousands of children in the attempt to define just how many disease-causing strains there were. In the course of these studies, more and more viruses began to turn up that were not polio. Some of them were found in patients and others in well persons; many of them were detectable only by their cytopathogenic effects in the tissue culture. Like the Coxsackie group, this family can cause various usually mild and transient illnesses in man. They were distinct from the Coxsackie family because the Coxsackies, in general, do not cause visible effects in tissue culture, while the tissue-culture group does not produce the characteristic syndrome in the newborn mouse. They were most remarkable, at least in the eyes of conventional virologists, for the lack of symptoms they caused and so came to be known as "viruses in search of a disease," or "orphans." In a meeting in 1955 they were formally christened the ECHO viruses: E for enteric because they are found in the intestinal tract, C for cytopathogenic, H for human, and O for orphan.

A few years later one of the ECHO viruses was discovered to be somewhat different in size and other characteristics from the rest of the group and so was redubbed reo, respiratory and enteric orphan. Since that time, two other reo's have been found and actually the reo's have proved to be the most common of all the known orphans.

The Adenoviruses

Enders' discoveries naturally stimulated the use of tissue culture for laboratory studies, and pressures began to increase for supplies of healthy human cells. Every day throughout the United States and other civilized countries hundreds of children are divested of their tonsils and adenoids, and Wallace Rowe of the National Institutes of Health began to wonder if these tissues, usually simply discarded, might not serve a useful purpose. To test this possibility, Rowe and his laboratory chief, Robert Huebner, made arrangements to procure the adenoids removed from children in hospitals in Washington, D.C., and to set them up in tissue-culture incubators, following Enders' method. At first the cells flourished but after about three weeks, more than half of the cultures began to degenerate, showing cytopathogenic effects, and in another week or ten days they were almost completely destroyed. If a filtrate from these degenerating cultures was transferred to a fresh batch of adenoidal tissue, identical cell destruction took place, but this time rapidly. New samples of tissue were tried and rigorous measures taken to obviate any possibility of virus contamination from outside sources, but still the effects occurred in the test tube. Apparently the adenoids had come complete with their own viruses, which were undetectable by ordinary means but which grew out in the incubator culture and made their presence known. These came to be known as the adenoviruses.

Some twenty-eight different human adenoviruses now have been isolated, mostly from children, and almost everyone has been found to have antibodies against several of them. They do produce diseases, a whole spectrum including conjunctivitis ("pink-eye"), laryngitis, and the all-too-familiar intestinal flu. Sometimes they appear to lie latent and asymptomatic for a long time and then flare up in an acute stage. More often, however, the children from whom they were isolated appeared completely healthy and no diseases showed up in a great variety of animals in which the viruses were tested. The adenoviruses joined the ranks of the human orphans in 1956.

So within the course of only a very few years—dating almost precisely from the moment Dalldorf held that neonatal mouse between thumb and forefinger for an injection of the virus from Coxsackie—the whole picture of virology changed. Viruses could no longer be defined, operationally speaking, as the agents of disease. Viruses were everywhere, part of the great substratum on which our biological existence rests. The more ways that one could devise for "seeing" them, the more that could be found and the number and variety seem to be without limit.

Cancer-associated Orphans

Soon the question of cancer began to enter the picture. Helene Wallace Toolan at the Sloan-Kettering Institute in New York City was injecting human cell fractions into newborn hamsters to test their immunological responses. A few weeks after her first experiments she was astonished to find among the hamster litters that about one in ten looked very peculiar. The young animals were stunted, their heads were small, their faces flattened, and their eyes and tongues protruded and they had frail, needle-like teeth or none at all. The syndrome somewhat resembled human mongolism. The bizarre group of effects was traced to a virus, present in the human cancer tissues, which attacked growing bone in the hamsters, causing the small skeleton and skull. Adult animals are not affected, and at higher doses in the newborns it is rapidly fatal, but just on the threshold of the fatal effects, it produces the strange deformities in the infants. It did not produce tumors in the hamsters or in any other animals in which it was tested.

When Toolan published her results, it turned out that the same virus had been discovered before by Lawrence Kilham, then of the National Institutes of Health. He had also found it in association with tumors, but with rat tumors, and since it did not cause cancers or any other obvious disease in the animals, he too had considered it an orphan, but a rat orphan. This raised the question, of course, as to whether Toolan really had a human virus or not, since the tumors with which she was working had been maintained in laboratory animals and might have picked up a contaminant. Besides, a fairly large survey of human sera from both cancer patients and well persons showed that humans in general lacked antibodies to the virus.

As a rigorous test of the humanness of the virus, Toolan set up an ingenious experiment involving the Royal Marsden Hospital in London, amply far away to still any rumors of contamination. She reasoned that if it was a human virus, but humans had no antibodies to it, this might occur because the virus was introduced into the body when it was still an embryo, before the antibody-forming ability developed. She made arrangements with the London hospital to save her the livers from the next 100 human embryos lost by miscarriage or therapeutic abortion. Each liver was frozen, and half of it sent to her and the other half sent as a control to the University of London. In one out of five of these, the mysterious orphan was found. So, its humanness was established beyond all doubt, but its effects on the human are as much of a mystery as ever. It would be interesting to know what disease, if any, the one in five might have developed in the course of a lifetime.

A second cancer-associated orphan was found by Vernon Riley also at Sloan-Kettering. In many cancer patients a number of enzymes which are ordinarily found in tissue appear in the blood stream; one of these is lactic dehydrogenase (LDH). These enzymes have been of interest for some years because of the hope they might serve as a cancer diagnostic test. This never worked out. The enzyme increases did not appear early enough in the course of the disease to aid in cancer detection, but some of them, LDH in particular, proved to be a sensitive indicator of cancer growth increasing as the tumor got larger or dropping quickly in response to therapy. It was generally assumed that the source of these enzymes was the cancer cells themselves which, in their chaotic growth, leaked materials into the blood stream, although there was no real proof of this assumption.

Riley began to examine mice with transplanted tumors and found that they, too, had increased LDH levels in the blood. Hundreds of mice bearing a total of more than forty different common laboratory tumors showed the increase, but it was seldom found in animals with spontaneous cancers or with tumors that had been induced by the application of chemicals. Following this clue, Riley was able to find that it is not the cancer alone that causes the increase in the enzyme, but a virus that travels with the cancer, presumably acquired as the tumor is transplanted from host to host. If this virus is injected into tumorless mice, a slight rise in the enzyme occurs, but if it is injected into a mouse with a spontaneous or induced tumor, the enzyme level soars up a hundred-fold or more, fluctuating, as does the enzyme in man, with the tumor growth. The agent does not itself cause cancer; in fact it does not cause anything detectable but the enzyme change, and its special relationship with the cancer cell is not yet understood. Whether or not the LDH found in the blood stream of so many human cancer patients signals the presence of a similar latent human virus is not known, but it does seem possible that Riley has uncovered either something new about cancer or a new technique that may let loose a new horde of unexpected orphans, or perhaps both.

SV40

Toward the end of the 1950s, many investigators concerned with the production of vaccines began to feel uneasy. Viruses were everywhere, and the fact that one did not always see them appeared to mean simply that one did not know how to look. In particular, the discovery of the adenoviruses as the silent inhabitants of cells in tissue culture raised some questions about use of such materials in the production of vaccines, particularly polio vaccine, which by then had been injected into thousands of young human hosts. Maurice Hilleman of Merck, one of the largest commercial manufacturers of the Salk vaccine, began to collect fluid from cultures of rhesus monkey kidney cells to see if he could find a virus in it. It proved disconcertingly simple. When filtrates of the rhesus cells were added to kidney cells of another species, the green monkey, cytopathogenic effects were seen. The responsible agent was given the name of vacuolating virus because of the typical holes or vacuoles it produces in the susceptible tissues. Later, since it was found to be very common in several kinds of monkeys, it came to be called simian virus 40, or SV40. When polio virus was harvested from the tissue cultures, studies showed, SV40 was harvested with it. The simian virus was much less sensitive to formalin, however, so it was not inactivated by the treatment that "killed" the polio virus in the commercial production of the Salk vaccine. Vaccine production was halted at two of the largest commercial laboratories, including Merck, until new procedures were adopted to exclude the simian orphan.

This was not the end, however. Within a short time, Bernice Eddy reported that a filtrate from rhesus monkey kidney cells caused tumors in newborn hamsters. The agent in the cancer-causing filtrate was identified by both Eddy's group and Hilleman's as SV40. SV40 is the first primate virus to produce cancers in the laboratory, and it is a potent agent. With sufficiently large doses of the virus, 100 per cent of the newborn hamsters develop fatal disease within a few weeks. Newborn mice have also proved susceptible to SV40, but no cancers attributable to it have been seen in monkeys or in man.

Joseph Melnick of Baylor pointed out the physical similarities among the viruses that cause rabbit papilloma, mouse polyoma, human warts, and SV40 and proposed that they be considered a single group or family of viruses, for which he suggested the name "papova" from *pa*pilloma, *po*lyoma, and *va*cuolating. (Since warts are also technically papillomas they are included in the *pa*.) Since that time it has been found that the Toolan-Kilham virus is also, from its physical characteristics, a member of the papova group.

John J. Trentin, also of Baylor University, began reflecting on the human cancer problem and on the great number of human orphan viruses. Among these human orphans, the most likely candidates for a cancer virus, in his estimation, were the adenoviruses. They were ubiquitous, latent in children, and somewhat resembled the polyoma and papilloma viruses in their physical make-up, although they are much larger. Trentin and his coworkers began systematically injecting adenoviruses into newborn hamsters, the host that was by then generally agreed to be the most sensitive to virus tumor induction. Among the first nine adenovirus types tested, one of these, adenovirus 12, produced cancers in eight out of ten of the animals tested, with fast-growing, highly malignant tumors appearing in one to three months. Shortly after, Huebner and Rowe confirmed Trentin's findings and reported similar results with adenovirus 18. Subsequently Trentin's group has tested the sera of 1200 humans of different ages and has found that forty-four per cent, almost half, have antibodies for adenovirus 12.

There is absolutely no evidence that any adenovirus causes any form of cancer in man, but it does lead one to pause and think, as Trentin did, about the possible nature of the human orphans.

13   The Transformers

Lysogeny, as very precisely defined in the bacterium-phage relationship, has never been proved to occur in animal cells, but there are animal cell-virus relationships that suggest it. The example that occurs to most clinical virologists is *Herpes simplex*, the virus that causes fever blisters or canker sores. Herpes apparently establishes itself early in the life of its host, since its effects are usually seen first in childhood, and spends most of its existence in hiding until something occurs that unbalances its relationship with the cell. Such an upset can be brought about by the ultraviolet irradiation of sunlight, fever, irritation, illness, fatigue, or even emotional upset. (Herpes eruptions have been induced during sessions in which a psychiatrist forced a patient to relive a trying emotional experience.) The herpes proliferates for a brief period, causing the familiar small ulcer, and then the infection subsides, the ulcer heals, and the virus goes back into hiding. Herpes victims have antibodies to the virus in their blood stream, but these cannot quell the local eruption, and some believe the virus may pass directly from one cell to another. Herpes is a DNA virus, like the temperate phage, but no evidence has been uncovered to indicate that it involves itself in any way with the cellular DNA, or that it even replicates except during periods of overt infection. The fact that ultraviolet can "induce" herpes is a provocative parallel, however, as is the induction of mouse leukemia virus by X-rays, although very little is known about the nature or habits of the elusive leukemia viruses.

Another agent long remarkable for its disappearance is

the Shope papilloma virus. It can be recovered with ease
from the warty growths of the cottontail but disappears
when it is injected into the domestic rabbit, in which it is
much more virulent, and when the papillomas turn to
cancer in either the cottontail or the domestic, the virus
is nowhere to be found.

The rabbit papillomas consist of a base of rapidly dividing tumor cells which merge into a warty outer layer in
which the cells do not divide but are constantly pushed
upward by the vigorously proliferating underlying tissue.
In 1957 Wilbur F. Noyes and Robert Mellors of the
Sloan-Kettering Institute, using a method originally developed by Albert H. Coons of Harvard, labeled antibodies
to the papilloma virus with a dye, fluorescein, that glows
under ultraviolet light. Cottontail rabbits with large
papillomas were injected with the fluorescein-tagged antibodies and their papillomas then removed. When specimens were illuminated with ultraviolet light and examined under the microscope, there was almost no trace
of fluorescence in the rapidly dividing cells, just a few
random spots here and there, although the warty outer
layer was stippled with bright apple-green antibodies. Apparently significant amounts of virus were produced only
in non-dividing cells, although the virus triggered the
rapid cell division. When similar studies were made in the
domestic rabbit, even fewer fluorescent antibodies were
found in the dividing cells, and when cancers were examined, there was just an occasional random spot which
did not appear to represent complete virus at all but just
some abortive scraps of protein coat. Apparently, just as
phage may "choose" to replicate or to lysogenize, this
virus "chooses" either to replicate or to disappear within
and so change its host cell.

By this time there had been great improvements in
tissue-culture techniques and in their applications to virology. Enders' group, which set all this in motion, established the usefulness of combinations of the new anti-

biotics to prevent bacterial contamination. A method first developed in 1916 by Peyton Rous was revived; it involves the use of trypsin to eat away the connective material in tissue fragments, leaving a suspension of isolated cells which then settle in a layer on the surface of the culture flask. Cultures that develop from a piece of tissue are, like the tissue, composed of many different cell types, but by trypsinization it is possible to grow out uniform sheets of similar cells or even to isolate a single cell and grow out a whole colony from it. (Such a colony of cells derived from a single ancestor is known as a clone.)

Renato Dulbecco of the California Institute of Technology was quick to recognize the resemblance between such cell colonies and the bacterial "lawns" that so greatly facilitated the sophisticated studies of the bacteriophage. Dulbecco worked out a method by which a very dilute suspension of the virus to be tested is incubated with the cells long enough for some of them to become infected. The unadsorbed virus is then washed off and the cells are overlaid with a thin layer of nutritive jelly-like material, or agar. The agar limits the spread of virus as it is released from the cell so that the new particles can infect only immediately adjacent cells; as a result, each time a virus sets up a cycle of infection, a discrete plaque or clearing appears in the layer of cells. This method makes it easy to count viable virus—since one plaque equals one original particle—and also to isolate pure line cultures readily. These new techniques opened the way to a whole series of new types of studies with the animal viruses.

When the trypsin-isolated cells settle on the glass or plastic surfaces of the culture flasks, they invariably organize themselves into orderly rows, no more than one layer thick. Cancer cells, on the other hand, growing under similar circumstances, pile up in multilayered, disorganized heaps. M. Abercrombie of University College, London, observing the isolated normal cells, noticed that when they first land on the smooth surface they tend to move about, traveling in one direction indefinitely until they touch another cell. When two cells meet, each turns away and starts off in the other direction until it touches another cell. Eventually, as the cells multiply, every one finds itself surrounded on all sides by neighbors and at this point ceases to try to move and settles down, soon adhering to the cells on either side of it and also to the surface of the container. Finally all the cells are immobilized, linked together in a regular meshwork. If part of the meshwork is scooped out, the cells will grow and move again to fill the defect, but otherwise cell division is rarely seen in the tight-knit colony.

A normal cell's aversion to running over another cell, which Abercrombie refers to as contact inhibition, seems to have something to do with the cell surface. A freely moving cell is preceded in its travels by a ruffled membrane, which he believes may be a part of its locomotive apparatus. It is this membrane that makes contact with the other cell, and at this moment of contact the normal cell stops. Cancer cells, presumably because of some difference of cell membrane, are not subject to contact inhibition.

In 1956 Robert Manaker and Vincent Groupé at Rutgers noticed that when chick embryo cells in tissue culture were injected with Rous sarcoma virus, some of them began to act like cancer cells, running over one another and piling up in little heaps. Harry Rubin became interested in this phenomenon when he was at the California Institute of Technology with Howard Temin in 1958 and continued to study it after he joined Stanley's laboratory at Berkeley. Rubin showed that these little heaps of cells are actually tiny tumors in the test tube. If inoculated into a young chick, they divide to form the characteristic Rous sarcoma.

Unlike most viruses, the Rous virus does not cause destructive effects when it multiplies in cells in tissue culture, and the cells continue to grow although releasing a slow steady trickle of virus. By the fluorescent antibody technique, it can be seen that the particles of tumor virus begin to form at the surfaces of the cells, after which they bud out through the cell membrane and then break away. Rubin suggested that the presence of the forming viruses along the cell membrane changes its properties and so releases the cell from the normal regulations of contact inhibition.

Polyoma Virus

In 1960 Dulbecco and a colleague, Marguerite Vogt, began to study the effects of polyoma virus on the tissue-culture monolayers. In the mouse cells, as Stewart and Eddy had observed several years before, most of the cells are destroyed and new virus is produced in large quantities. Vogt and Dulbecco noticed that a few of these cells survive, and as these survivors multiply, they begin to pile up and take on the characteristics of tumor cells, or, to use the phrase that became current at this time, they become transformed.

Hamster cells in tissue culture also undergo transformation, as Vogt and Dulbecco reported at the same time. Unlike the mouse cells, none of them lyse nor do they support the growth of the virus, but a small number change shape and pile up to become microtumors. Transformation in the hamster cells can be shown to be caused by infectious DNA as well as by the intact virus.

The change to cancer seems to take place in two distinct steps, which they compare to the steps to papilloma and then to cancer with the Shope virus. First, the cells begin to grow rapidly and irregularly. Then, in the second phase, they lose contact inhibition and chromosome changes appear. At this second stage, but not before, they produce tumors when inoculated into laboratory animals. Cells transformed by the polyoma virus will not produce virus particles nor can they be induced to produce them by X-rays, ultraviolet light, or chemicals. If they are infected with more polyoma virus, however, they will support its growth.

Karl Habel of the National Institutes of Health found that cells transformed by the polyoma virus have a new surface antigen not related to any antigen of the virus which, like the *Salmonella* antigens, are characteristic of the transformed cell. It is absolutely specific and occurs regardless of the type of cell or the species of animal or whether infection takes place in tissue culture or in the normal host.

Transformation, at least with the polyoma virus, is a rare event. In the hamster cells, which are the most susceptible known, only about ten per cent become transformed when the cells are flooded with virus. Michael Stoker of the University of Glasgow has calculated that nearly a million polyoma virus particles are present for each cell that is transformed; yet transformation seems to be effected by just one particle. One wonders whether this one-in-a-million particle is somehow different from the others or if it meets with some extraordinary circumstances when it penetrates the cell. Pretreatment of the hamster cells with X-rays considerably increases the sensitivity of the surviving cells to transformation by polyoma virus, perhaps because of the chromosome breakage that the X-rays cause.

SV40

In 1962, the year after the report that SV40 caused tumors in newborn hamsters, Enders with his associate Harvey Shein showed that human kidney cells as well as mouse kidney cells support the growth of SV40 in tissue culture. After sixty days or more, when most of the original cells had disappeared, changed cells began to appear in the culture, Shein and Enders observed, and these cells, by all previous criteria, were transformed. Hilary Koprowski of the Wistar Institute, who noted transformation in human cell cultures at almost the same time as Enders and Shein, took a further step. He removed cell samples from human donors, grew them in tissue culture, and then inoculated the culture with SV40. Some of these cells became transformed, and these he implanted back under the skin of the original donors. They grew into small nodules before he removed them, and one of these nodules had the appearance under the microscope of a sarcoma. This is as close as science has come to experimentally producing cancer in man by a virus.

SV40 also transforms hamster kidney cells and, like the polyoma-transformed cells, the hamster cells can be shown to have a new antigen distinct from the antigen of the virus. SV40 transformed cells produce infectious particles only very rarely. They can be passed from one tissue culture to another for many transfers without a trace of virus being found, and then suddenly virus particles are released into the culture fluid. Or an SV40 tumor can be passed from hamster to hamster for many passages without any sign of virus in the animals until suddenly an animal will show up that has antibodies to the virus.

Paul Gerber of the National Institutes of Health, in a search for the hidden virus, removed SV40-induced tumors from hamsters and grew the cells in tissue culture. No infectious virus particle could be detected. Then he seeded similar cells directly onto a tissue culture of kidney cells from the green monkey. The characteristic vacuoles appeared in the culture, with the changes appearing first in the kidney cells that were next to the tumor cells. Then he repeated the experiment, seeding the tumor cells this time onto a layer of rabbit kidney cells. These cells cannot be infected by the whole virus but they can be infected by the viral DNA. In the mixed cell culture, intact viral particles again appeared. Apparently the SV40 transformed cells contain the viral nucleic acid, but this must make its way into some other cell before it can replicate to form complete infectious particles.

Huebner has shown that antigens characteristic for the virus can be found in cancer cells produced by adenoviruses or by SV40. More recently, Mary Fink of the National Cancer Institute has prepared fluorescent antibodies against mouse leukemia virus and, by this technique, has been able to demonstrate the presence of viral antigen within the mouse leukemic cells.

Rous Sarcoma Virus

The Rous sarcoma virus differs from the other transforming viruses in its nucleic acid, which is RNA rather than DNA, and also in the rapidity and efficiency with which it produces malignant transformation. In tissue culture, transformed cells appear within one or two days and nearly all of the cells infected are transformed. Similarly, when RSV, as it is known by modern investigators, is injected into a chicken, typical sarcoma cells develop at the site of injection within forty-eight hours and a palpable tumor in five or six days. As Rubin says, RSV is a specialist in carcinogenesis.

In the course of studies with the virus in tissue culture, Rubin and his associates from time to time came across cultures in which no transformation could be produced and little or no virus grew. After this occurred a number of times, they ceased attributing it to bad luck or to technical error and so discovered that the virus would not grow because the embryos from which the cells had been taken for the culture were already infected with a virus. This virus, which came to be known as RIF, for resistance-inducing factor, turned out to be one of the chicken leukosis viruses. These viruses are common latent viruses in fowl and, unlike the Rous virus, rarely cause cancer and do not produce transformation or other changes in the ordinary chick cell tissue culture.

With the discovery of RIF, Rubin began to worry about the fact that cells that have once been infected with RSV cannot be reinfected with RSV. Postulating that this resistance might be due not to RSV itself but to some contaminating virus, Hidesaburo Hanafusa, then a graduate student in his laboratory, prepared very dilute suspensions of RSV so as to spread the particles far apart over the tissue-culture monolayer, making it probable that a given cell could not be infected by more than one virus particle of either RSV or contaminant. Then, during the eclipse period, which is some twelve hours long with these viruses, individual infected cells were moved to fresh cultures.

The first of the two postulated viruses was relatively easy to isolate by this method. It multiplied readily in tissue culture, did not produce any transformations, and induced resistance to RSV infection; like RIF, it proved to be one of the fowl leukosis viruses. It was promptly christened RAV, for Rous-associated virus.

The second virus proved much more difficult to capture. When transformed cells were isolated and transplanted, they grew readily but they either released no virus whatsoever or they released both viruses, RAV and the transforming virus. It was beginning to seem as if RAV was necessary for the production of RSV. To test this hypothesis, RAV was added to a focus of transformed cells that were not producing virus, and viruses promptly appeared, both of them.

When RAV and RSV were compared, they looked suspiciously alike. In fact, they were immunologically identical, meaning, of course, that they were wearing the same protein coat. RSV can obviously replicate its own genome; if one RSV-transformed cell is allowed to divide into thousands of cells, any one of these cells will release the RSV genome when superinfected with RAV. But apparently it cannot make protein coats although not averse to appropriating any that are available. More recently

Rubin and Hanafusa have found that not just RAV but all of the leukosis viruses tested can rescue RSV from inside the transformed cell, and RSV in such cases wears the characteristic overcoat tailored by that leukosis virus. So, if Rubin is right, the classic tumor virus and the "specialist in carcinogenesis" is not a complete virus at all, by any conventional definition, but just a vagrant bit of nucleic acid.

One is tempted to weave a connection between the defectiveness of the Rous sarcoma virus and its transforming ability and, even better, between the Rous sarcoma virus and the other transforming viruses. This temptation is made more alluring by some experimental suggestions that RSV, though not RAV, might actually contain DNA rather than RNA. This is difficult to establish conclusively since the Rous particles, being extremely fragile, have defied complete isolation and purification for years, and they are always found in mixtures with RAV particles which outnumber them ten to one. It may well be true that RSV is carcinogenic because of its defectiveness, which forces it to "choose" a lingering relationship with the cell, and it is perhaps even true that it is a DNA virus, but, as Marcel Baluda from the City of Hope Medical Center has shown recently, one of the avian leukosis viruses, an RNA virus, and, in fact, one of those same viruses that can rescue RSV, produces transformations in cultures of appropriate chick embryo cells. So it is clearly not necessary to be defective or to be DNA to be a transformer.

Luria once described viruses as "bits of heredity in search of a chromosome," and, as Eugene Wollman glimpsed many years ago, there are biological relationships in which infection and heredity merge so completely that one can no longer distinguish between them. In some instances cancer would appear to be the result of such a relationship.

Part IV

WORK IN PROGRESS

14   Art and Architecture

For fifteen years or more after the development of the electron microscope in the early 1940s, the structure of the animal viruses remained virtually unknown. Despite the high resolving power of the instrument, the particles are so small and light that they are virtually transparent to the electron beam and, to add to the difficulties, the earlier procedures used in preparing the specimens often distorted them.

Crick and Watson suggested that the protein coats of viruses would prove to be composed of a number of identical units repeated over and over again. They reasoned that because viruses carry only a small amount of hereditary information, they would use that information as economically as possible and would not make a vast number of proteins or a huge and complicated molecule when a relatively small and simple one would do.

Although the long slim cylinders of tobacco mosaic and the improbable tadpoles of the T-even phage rendered them outstanding and readily identifiable from the beginning, the details of their composition were not known, and no matter how greatly magnified, the viruses that attack man and the other vertebrates stubbornly resembled dots and blobs and balls of cotton.

During the early 1950s, the microscopists began a serious attack on the problem. "The essential common to all endeavors," Peter Wildy of Glasgow University points out, "was prophesied by Carroll in 1876:

> 'You boil it with sawdust; you salt it with glue:
> 'You condense it with locusts and tape:

'Still keeping one principal object in view—
'To preserve its symmetrical shape.'"

In keeping with this objective, Robley Williams in 1953 introduced a new method of freeze-drying which seemed to prevent the particles from collapsing. C. E. Hall of the Massachusetts Institute of Technology reported in 1955 that osmium and certain other metals would impregnate or "stain" the particles and make them more electron-opaque so they would stand out with more contrast. Controversy began to brew about their geometry, and Williams hit upon the idea of photographing not the virus particles themselves but their shadows. He sprayed the particles from an angle with vaporized metal. The vapor coated the side of the particle facing the spray gun and also the surface beyond it, but in the region just behind the particle a "shadow" was left where the vapor could not reach, just like the shadow cast when bright

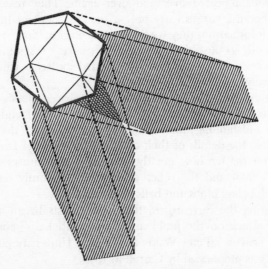

Figure 13. Diagram of virus particle showing how double shadowing technique can reveal the viral geometry. (After a drawing in *Scientific American*.)

sunlight strikes an object at an angle. When electron micrographs were taken of the shadowed particles, the electrons were able to penetrate most completely where the metal did not, and so a sharp silhouette of the virus was produced. By spraying the same particle from two different angles, Williams found, he was able to compare the outlines of different surfaces of the same particle and so to understand their geometry.

TMV was the first virus shown to fulfill the prediction of Watson and Crick. The protein of TMV, it is now known, consists of almost 2200 identical submolecules, known as structure units, each made up of a chain of 158 amino acids. Chains of amino acids can fold themselves into a variety of shapes, known as their tertiary structure. The submolecule of TMV is, as Fraenkel-Conrat describes it, "football-shaped." At the narrower end of the "football" is an area, a chemical groove, into which fits the strand of RNA. These structure units, attracted by the RNA and by each other form a circle, like the petals on a daisy, and the RNA strand coils to run through the "groove." But within this circle there is just room for sixteen of the units, with a little room left over, so when the seventeenth structure unit joins the aggregate, it lies a little bit on the top of the first one, and hence a new circle has to start. For each full 360° turn of the RNA, there are sixteen and one third units, and when all are assembled a helix of 2200 protein units has formed and, poised within them, coiled some 130 times around, is the molecule of RNA. And, as careful mathematical calculations have shown, the particle is just as long as and no longer than this coiled strand of nucleic acid. This then is the Stanley unit.

Within a brief span of time, the prediction of Crick and Watson was found to hold true for a number of other viruses as well. X-ray diffraction data suggested that the viruses that appeared to be round were not just lumps but that they had some kind of cubic symmetry. These observations agreed again with Crick and Watson, who had pointed out that if the structure units of these viruses were to assemble themselves—as they should for maximum operating efficiency—they would have to be packed in a symmetrical pattern. Such symmetry, it was known, could be achieved only in a figure that had four sides, eight sides, or twenty sides; of these three possibilities, the twenty-sided figure, an icosahedron, offered the most efficient possible packaging arrangement for a large number of small particles, producing the maximum internal capacity. It is interesting to reflect that during this period architect Buckminster Fuller was exploring these same problems for superficially different reasons.

By the use of the special shadowing techniques, Williams worked out the structure of the "spherical" virus *Tipula iridescent*, a large insect virus. *Tipula* turned out to be an icosahedron, each side of which was an equilateral triangle, with 812 separate subunits symmetrically arranged in a beautiful geodesic dome. And so far all the other "spherical" viruses whose geometry has been determined have proved to be twenty-sided.

In 1959 Brenner and Horne introduced a technique known as negative staining, which has brought about tremendous advances in the knowledge of the fine details of viruses. As in Hall's positive staining technique, the "dye" used is a metal, but in this case a metal that does not interact with the particles. The metal, usually phosphotungstate, and the virus are sprayed together onto a flat surface with the result that the virus particle ends up embedded in and surrounded by the phosphotungstate. The metal, which does not permit the electrons to pass, fills in the cracks and crevices around the outside of the virus and even enters hollow spaces within the shell so that the electron beam can pass only through the virus particle. One of the first triumphs of the technique was to make visible the components of the tail of the T4 phage, and much of the new information about the animal viruses has similarly been gained by this method.

During this same period, methods for the preparation of tissues for electron microscopy also were improved. It became possible to take plastic-embedded specimens and make uniform slices only 200 or 300 Angstroms thick right through a cell and through any of the larger viruses that happened to be in the path of the cell-slicer, or microtome. Once cytologists began to be able to identify the normal components of the cell, some of which—such as ribosomes —are not very dissimilar in size and appearance from the viruses, virologists began to be able to trace viruses within the cell during the visible phases of their life cycles. Councilman Morgan of Columbia University's College of Physicians and Surgeons, who has probably worked longer and more successfully at the electron microscopy of the virus within the cell than anyone else, recently introduced a method for making viruses somewhat visible to the electron microscope even during their eclipse period. The key to the method is a large protein molecule, ferritin, which contains a tiny pellet of iron about fifty-five Angstroms in diameter that shows up as a firm black dot in the electron micrograph. Ferritin does not interfere with the normal properties and activities of antibodies but enables the electron microscope to track them in the cell. As a consequence, antibodies prepared against viral fragments and tagged with ferritin will reveal the localization within the infected cell of various invisible viral substructures.

Classification of Viruses

In the early decades of virology, classification of viruses, since it could not be based on their anatomical characteristics as is done with other biological systems, had to depend upon tissues infected and symptoms produced. Even in the beginning, this was unsatisfactory; yellow fever, for example, attacks the viscera in man, the nervous system in the mouse, and multiplies harmlessly in the mosquito. By the 1950s the system became hopelessly inadequate with the discovery of scores of new viruses which caused any of a number of different syndromes or, more bewilderingly, none at all.

By this time the sizes of many of the common viruses had become known. The unit of measurement for viruses is usually either the millimicron, which is one ten-millionth of a centimeter, or the Angstrom, which is one-tenth of a millimicron. These sizes are much too small to be imaginable but are useful for comparative purposes. A red blood cell, the smallest human cell, is huge on this scale, some 75,000 Angstroms in diameter; the largest bacteria is about 7500 Angstroms, the largest virus 2800 Angstroms, the smallest about 200 Angstroms, and a hemoglobin molecule about 150 Angstroms. The different methods of preparing viruses for electron microscopy affect their apparent sizes and, furthermore, calibration of electron microscopes is still somewhat uncertain, which is why the exact dimensions of some of the viruses are still not established, but size ranges are defined.

Further, it was becoming clear that a common feature of all viruses was a nucleic acid core surrounded by an outer shell of protein; these two together are known as the nucleocapsid. Lwoff proposed as a working definition that the term "virus" be restricted to agents that contained protein and either DNA or RNA, but not both; this did not advance knowledge but served usefully to exclude certain larger organisms, such as the agents of trachoma and parrot fever, which had been hovering on the borders of virology for many years and blurring their outlines. Whether a virus contained RNA or DNA became a salient point of identification. Also it was soon found that some viruses, like herpes and influenza, were surrounded by additional envelopes which serve to distinguish them (see Plate 5). Committees of virologists, for whom the chief spokesman has been Mill Hill's C. H. Andrewes, set out to classify the viruses on the basis of the incoming data concerning their sizes, shapes, and chemistry. This not only provides a useful way for writing and talking about viruses but also it has revealed some new and unexpected relationships and, as a consequence, sparked some new ideas. Eight groups have now been generally decided upon which comprise some 350 of the known viruses of vertebrates.

The largest viruses are those of the pox family, which includes smallpox, vaccinia, and rabbit myxoma and fibroma (see Plates 5 and 6). All of these viruses can be classed together on the basis of their morphology and also, it can be observed, all have a tendency to produce cellular proliferation as well as the tissue-destroying lesions for which some of them are better known. The newest member of this group is the Yaba monkey tumor virus. Its effects were first formally noted in 1957 when an epidemic of subcutaneous tumors occurred in a colony of rhesus monkeys at the laboratories of the West African Council for Medical Research in Lagos, Nigeria. The tumors were clearly infectious—twenty out of thirty-five of the monkeys developed them—and clearly benign, since the growths all regressed spontaneously in a few weeks. Samples of the tumors were sent to Andrewes who isolated the virus from them.

Pox Viruses

The pox viruses are DNA viruses with an outer envelope. The DNA is double-stranded, wound in the helical arrangement described by Watson and Crick. The vaccinia virus, which is the most studied of the group and therefore its prototype, has a dense inner core that, in the mature particle, is usually in the shape of a dumbbell; this is composed of nucleic acid and protein. A protein coat surrounds the dumbbell and on the outside of that is usually an envelope made of lipoprotein, the material that forms the outer membrane of the cell. (See Plate 5.)

Apparently only the large bacteriophage have tails that serve as an injection mechanism; this seems to be their special adaptation for dealing with the barrier presented by the tough and relatively inflexible cell wall. As far as is known, all animal viruses, including pox, are taken into the cell, protein coat and all, so the removal of the membrane, if any, and the protein capsid is one of the necessary first steps in viral infection. In the case of the pox viruses, as Wolfgang Joklik of the Albert Einstein College of Medicine has shown, the host cell obligingly produces a new enzyme designed especially to free the lethal DNA. With the other viruses, it would appear to be the ordinary digestive enzymes of the cells that strip away the virus coat.

Once stripped, the virus is no longer visible but some hours later, within the infected cells, virus "factories" begin to appear in which new virus particles can be seen in the process of formation. These factories were called "inclusion bodies" by the light microscopists, to whom they were readily visible. In the 1920s, inclusion bodies received a great deal of attention as a means of diagnosing and studying viral diseases, but so much controversy sprang up as to whether they were or were not the viruses themselves that the whole subject fell into disrepute and was abandoned. After being completed in the factory, virus particles may be shipped to the cell wall and released or, as is the case particularly with the pox viruses, may remain in association with the cell until it disintegrates.

In 1936 George Berry and Helen Dedrick of the University of Rochester showed that animals inoculated simultaneously with myxoma virus that had been inactivated with heat, so that it would no longer cause infection, and with live fibroma virus would come down with the lethal myxomatosis. This was thought at that time to be perhaps another example of transformation, such as Griffith had first shown with the pneumococci, but in the light of later knowledge it would seem that the fibroma virus probably "rescues" some of the myxoma particles by carrying out some of the functions that the heat-altered agent can no longer accomplish. It has since been found that most of the viruses of the pox group can reactivate one another in this way.

Myxoviruses

Next, in order of size, are the myxoviruses, so-called because of their affinity for mucous (myxo) substances on the surfaces of the cells they infect. In 1941 George K. Hirst of the Rockefeller Foundation Virus Laboratory was working with influenza virus in the fertilized egg and accidentally mixed some of the virus-filled fluid with fresh-spilled embryonic blood. The red blood cells, he noticed, clumped rapidly together. Hemagglutination, as it is called technically, was subsequently found to be the result of the virus particles' sticking to the surfaces of the red blood cells until eventually a latticework forms of cells bridged by virus particles. Since it occurs almost immediately and is easily visible to the naked eye, it provided a useful and rapid test for the presence of virus at a time when such a test was sorely needed. Hemagglutination also permitted a rough estimate of the number of particles—judged by the amount of red blood cells agglutinated—and could reveal the presence of antibodies, since viruses cannot bind to red cells, and probably not to any other cells, when muffled in antibodies.

Many other viruses were eventually found to be hemagglutinators, but the myxoviruses are unique in that, after a short period of time, the blood cells spontaneously separate again and then, for a period of time, are resistant to viral hemagglutination. This is due, it was found, to an enzyme, neuraminidase, that eats away part of the cell

surface and presumably part of the virus' equipment for gaining entry into the host cell. Studies with the isolated enzyme have shown that the neuraminidase destroys the cell's receptor sites for the virus; once these are gone, the particle can no longer bind to the cell. Philip Marcus of the Albert Einstein College of Medicine, who has studied this phenomenon in tissue culture, reports that loss of the receptor sites does not seem to affect the health of the cell in any way, but he has found that the cell promptly destroys its invulnerability by repairing its receptor sites.

The myxoviruses, which include influenza, mumps, measles, and distemper are classified in two groups according to size. Their central core is made up of RNA with protein subunits arranged along it in a helix, as in the tobacco mosaic virus, although the coils of the myxovirus appear to be far more flexible than those of the stiff rod-like tobacco mosaic virus. (See Plates 6 and 7.) This nucleocapsid is surrounded by a lipoprotein envelope through which protrudes an array of stubby protein spikes. These spikes cover the surface of the particle so it somewhat resembles a sea cucumber in some of the micrographs, and the tips of the spikes, which make contact with the cell surface prior to infection, are believed to contain the neuraminidase. The envelope is usually vaguely spherical in shape but in the case of some of the influenza viruses, it may also assume a filamentous shape.

The life cycle of the virus is correspondingly complex and in fact structure and development are probably closely related. Some of the influenza virus is put together in the nucleus of the infected cell and, according to Morgan's ferritin antibody technique, this would appear to be the nucleoprotein. The hemagglutinating proteins, on the other hand, are made in the cytoplasm. The various parts of the virus are then assembled, apparently right on the cell's outer membrane; virus-infected cells grown in tissue culture can assemble red cells around them, Marcus has shown, because of the hemagglutinating virus protein accumulated at the cell surface, but none of this can be seen until the complete particles appear, always on the outermost edges of the cell. The outer envelope appears to be composed of portions of the outer membrane of the infected cell and it is picked up only as the virus particle leaves its host. In myxoinfected cells, viruses bubble off from the cell surface for as long as thirty hours after infection.

Studies of the RNA of the influenza virus indicate that, unlike the nucleic acid of bacteriophage and of other animal viruses studied, it may possibly be in more than one piece. Hirst recently suggested that maybe the nucleoprotein core of the virus is actually a random collection of pieces. This would explain several peculiarities about influenza, such as the high number of non-infective particles and the difficulty in demonstrating an infective RNA. Most pertinent, it could account for the extraordinary mutability of the virus and the high rate of recombination observed by Burnet since, if the nucleic acid were in pieces, it would be very easy in a cell infected by two different but genetically compatible strains for new combinations of the genetic material to arise.

Another member of the myxovirus family is swine influenza, a disease in which Shope has been interested for many years. As far as anyone knows, nothing like it ever appeared in swine before the late summer of 1918 when millions of pigs came down with the disease and thousands died of it. It now recurs annually. Shope proposed, and most generally now agree, that swine influenza is actually human influenza A, the influenza that was so widely prevalent in man during that epidemic, that has adapted itself to a new host, and he has turned up two curious factors in the disease. One is that the typical symptoms are not produced by the virus only but by a combination of the virus and a common bacillus, also virtually harmless alone. The other, discovered by Shope in the course of trying to find out where the swine in-

fluenza goes in the spring and summer, is that the agent
has a complex life cycle involving the lungworm, a parasite of the swine respiratory tract, which in turn has an
intermediate host in the earthworm which is eaten by
pigs that are permitted to root around in the soil. The
still-to-be-answered question, of course, is where human
influenza goes when it is not epidemic, and Shope's findings raise the question of whether or not swine might be
a natural reservoir for the disease.

Arboviruses and Adenoviruses

The arboviruses (short for arthropod-borne) resemble the myxo group in that they are RNA viruses surrounded by a lipoprotein envelope, although they are
smaller. They are all carried by insects, usually mosquitoes
or ticks. This group includes yellow fever, dengue, and
many of the other agents whose names carry that particular romantic aura of explorations and jungle adven-
tures. They multiply in their insect vectors as distinct,
for instance, from the myxoma virus, for which the mosquito is just a "flying needle." Many of these viruses are
antigenically related; in fact, it is often difficult to tell
where one strain begins and another ends, and it is believed that they probably stem from one common ancestor with the different strains evolving just as, on a higher
level, there evolved the different species of animals and
plants. The 1964 epidemic of St. Louis encephalitis that
affected some 10,000 and killed more than a score of persons in Houston alone was caused by a member of this
family.

The other classified viruses, both RNA and DNA, are
all icosahedrons, geometrically symmetrical and twenty-
sided. The first of the animal viruses to prove to be
icosahedral was the adeno family, which is an absolute
geometrical delight. (See Plate 8.) Each of the twenty
facets of the adenovirus shell is an equilateral triangle

with a subunit, or capsomere, in each corner of the triangle and four along each side. Six more capsomeres, divided into rows of one, two, and three each to form a
pyramid, fill in the center of the triangle. The capsomeres
along each edge are shared by the adjoining triangle and
those in each corner are shared by five triangles. This all
makes a total, for those who like to figure such things out,
of 252 separate capsomeres. Twenty-eight human adenoviruses have been identified and half a dozen more that
affect other vertebrates, and they are all very uniform in
size and appearance. The adenoviruses multiply in the
nucleus where they line up in an orderly crystalline array
—as many as 10,000 in a single cell—until eventually the
cell falls apart and sets them free.

The combination of adenovirus and cell produces a
new protein and this protein, it has been found, is a toxin
which is the cause of the major damage to the cells infected by the adenovirus. In tissue cultures, when the
adenovirus toxin is formed, the usually spindle-shaped
cells begin to grow round and then they clump together
and start to aggregate in large masses that detach from
the glass surface on which they are growing. It is these
effects that first revealed their presence to Rowe and
Huebner in the adenoids of the Washington, D.C. schoolchildren. Obviously toxin and virus usually come together,
but they are not difficult to separate. The toxin alone, it
has been found, will produce the characteristic effects on
the cells, but no new particles appear and eventually the
cells recover. If the virus alone is added to the culture,
the virus replicates and new particles appear, but aside
from the nuclear inclusions there are no changes in the
cell until enough of the toxin accumulates.

Herpes

The largest of the icosahedral viruses is the herpes
group, which includes herpes simplex, the familiar virus

of the cold sore or fever blister, and another which is known either as herpes varicella or herpes zoster, since, depending on the host that it encounters, it may cause either chicken pox (varicella) or shingles. Although the agent is identical, from the point of view of the victim, the two effects seem very different. Chicken pox, is, of course, a mild disease confined chiefly to children. An adult who is exposed to a child with chicken pox often will not come down with a systemic infection, presumably because of circulating antibodies, but may get a local infection of the nerve roots. Different areas of the body are supplied by different nerves that branch off the spinal cord between the vertebrae. Typically, herpes zoster involves just one of these branches, usually one feeding the central portion of the trunk of the body. The virus travels along the nerves to the skin where it causes the poxy rash typical of chicken pox, but in the case of zoster the rash is confined just to that area of the skin supplied by that particular dorsal or cranial nerve and actually can be used by the neurophysiologist to map such areas, or dermatomes. Shingles often occurs in persons who seem to have had no possible recent exposure to chicken pox and it is believed that this may be due to reactivation of some long latent virus, perhaps caused by injury to a nerve root, such as by a tumor, by other trauma, by cold or some other disease. Shingles can be very painful and, particularly when it involves a cranial nerve, may sometimes cause a temporary paralysis.

The shell of herpes virus is composed of 162 capsomeres, each one of which is made up in turn of five or six rodlike structure units that are "bundled together like faggots," as Wildy describes them, with a hollow core in the center that shows up quite distinctly in negatively stained particles. (See Plates 9 and 10.)

Herpes viruses form in the nucleus, where they cause characteristic destructive changes, and then pass out through the nuclear membrane. The particle is then transported inside of a vacuole or bubble which carries it to the cell surface and sets it free, like a diver escaping from a submarine.

Papova and Picorna Viruses

The papova group of viruses, a classification first proposed by Melnick, closely resembles the adenoviruses in physical appearance, which is one of the reasons why Trentin was led to seek tumor-inducing activity in the adeno group. All of the papova viruses, which include polyoma, Shope papilloma, SV40, and the virus of human warts, are known to cause tumors, either benign or malignant, except for one which is the virus discovered by Toolan in association with human cancers, which has never been proved to be a cancer-inducer. These viruses all have a core of double-stranded DNA.

The smallest of the icosahedrons are the picorna viruses, pico for little, plus RNA, which makes up their genetic material. The picornas are a very large family with some 100 members, including the three strains of polio, the Coxsackie and ECHO viruses and various encephalitis and enteroviruses of animals and birds. (See Plates 11 and 12.) These viruses have an outer shell of about thirty capsomeres and an inner core composed of a single strand of RNA. Like the other small viruses, the picorna viruses seem to be entirely dependent on the good offices of the host to gain entry to the cell. Cell and virus are first attracted to one another by electrostatic forces. When the virus becomes attached to the membrane, it appears to "tickle" it, as John Holland of the University of Washington describes it. The membrane retreats a little, curling in and taking the virus with it until a small depression forms beneath the particle. It sinks in deeper until the virus is sitting in a little pouch or cove surrounded on three sides by cell membrane. Then cytoplasmic arms form and clasp around the particle. The cell membrane surrounding the virus is pinched off and the Trojan horse is completely within the walls.

Holland confirms that it is, above all, viral receptors that determine innate susceptibility to a virus. Infectious RNA from polio virus, which can slip into a cell bypassing the receptor sites, can set up a growth cycle in the cell of any warm-blooded animal, but once the cycle is completed and intact protein-coated virus particles are produced, the cycle is finished, because they cannot reinfect. In other words, polio is a virus of primates simply because it can gain access only to primate cells. (Interestingly, when one gets farther down the evolutionary scale, polio cannot grow in fish, frog, or plant cells, protozoa or bacteria.) When cells are grown in tissue culture, Holland has shown, they may develop new receptor sites, presumably as a result of surface changes resulting from their freedom of contact with surrounding cells. Then they can readily support polio growth, which seems to explain why monkey kidney cells, for example, which are not ordinarily hosts for polio in the intact animal, serve the purpose so well in tissue culture.

Reo

The newest of the virus families is the reo group, the respiratory enteric orphans. These are medium-sized icosahedrons, but differ from all of the other vertebrate viruses known in that they contain RNA, which, instead of being in a single strand, is in a double helix similar to the Watson-Crick DNA helix. In fact, this is, with one exception, the only double-stranded RNA known that has more than a fleeting biological existence. This exception is the so-called wound tumor virus that produces tumors in stems and leaves of many different types of plants. It is carried by a mosquito-sized insect, the leaf hopper. Peter Gomatos and Igor Tamm of The Rockefeller Institute postulate that because of the close resemblance of the wound tumor and reo viruses, and because the double-stranded RNA might give the genetic material a special stability that would make it more likely to persist within the cell and so perhaps transform it, that the respiratory enteric orphans of man may also be cancer producers.

The Mavericks

A number of viruses remain unclassified, including rabies, which looks like a small myxo or perhaps a large arbo type, the avian leukemia viruses, and infectious mononucleosis and infectious hepatitis, neither of which have ever been seen or grown in a regularly reproducible fashion in the laboratory and which have been shown to be viral in nature only through rather heroic experiments recalling the early yellow-fever investigations in which the disease has been passed from human to human by means of filtrates. The hepatitis viruses are particularly troublesome not only because of their chronically debilitating effects but because the prevalence of the serum hepatitis strain in a latent form is presently a major hazard of blood transfusions and a chief obstacle to the use of this otherwise safe and often lifesaving procedure.

A virus that has been under particularly close recent scrutiny is that of German measles (rubella), which has such heartbreaking effects on the eyes, ears, and brains of the developing fetus. German measles has recently been found to contain RNA and, in appearance, to resemble the myxoviruses, but it seems to be unique in its vicious predilection for the unborn. Other viruses also may traverse the placenta, and occasionally a mother who has smallpox or chicken pox, for instance, late in pregnancy may give birth to a baby with a full-blown case of the disease, but these do not cause effects in the early stages as does rubella.

At present, a new virus family seems to be forming that is made up of the various mouse leukemia viruses, all of which have the same general appearance under the electron microscope, all of which, like the avian leukemia viruses, contain RNA, and many of which seem to be antigenically related. At one time, some of the mouse leukemia viruses, such as the Moloney agent, seemed to have tails, but these are now generally agreed to be distortions of the viral membrane produced when the particles are prepared for electron microscopy. Recently particles resembling the viruses of mouse leukemia have been isolated from the blood and tissues of patients with leukemia. It is of course not known whether or not these have anything to do with causing the disease, but if they prove to be physically and chemically very similar, the implications would be difficult to ignore, as the correlations between how viruses look, and how they behave and how they multiply within the cell, and their interactions with their host grow closer and stronger.

Even the visionary Beijerinck would have been considerably surprised had he ever glimpsed what a marvelous variety of creatures were contained in the contagium vivum fluidum he first isolated not so very long ago. In fact, until just the last decade or so, any notion of classifying viruses on the basis of their somatotypes would have been received with scorn. But what is really interesting is not that such a classification is technically feasible but that the usually abstract and pedantic science of taxonomy has proved to be one of virology's most fertile sources of new ideas.

CLASSIFICATIONS OF THE VIRUSES OF VERTEBRATES

Class	Size (in Angstroms)	Nucleic Acid	Multiplication site	Shape of Nucleocapsid	Envelope	Diseases
Pox	2200 × 2800	DNA	cytoplasm	helix	+	smallpox, vaccinia, myxomatosis, rabbit fibromas, Yaba monkey tumor
Myxo I	2000	RNA	nucleus	helix	+	measles, mumps, distemper
II	800	RNA	nucleus and cytoplasm	helix	+	influenza
Herpes	1300–1800	DNA	nucleus	icosahedron	+	fever blister, cold sores, shingles, chicken pox
Reo	750	RNA	cytoplasm	icosahedron	−	mild respiratory and intestinal infections
Adeno	700	DNA	nucleus	icosahedron	−	mild respiratory infections
Papova	450	DNA	nucleus	icosahedron	−	human warts, Shope papilloma, rabbit fibroma, polyoma, SV40, hamster mongoloid syndrome
Arbo	200–500	RNA	cytoplasm	?	+	yellow fever, dengue fever, St. Louis encephalitis
Picorna	250	RNA	cytoplasm	icosahedron	−	polio, Coxsackie, ECHO

15   Chemotherapy

When Delbrück began his studies in the late 1930s, he turned his back on the long and barren controversy as to the "utility" of the bacteriophage and he and his colleagues set out on the heady pursuit of knowledge for its own sake. While so doing, they blazed a shining trail for others to follow. Now, with the development of new techniques, it is becoming possible for virologists to study the animal viruses in much the same way that the earlier workers investigated the private life of the T-even phage. But there is a difference. No longer "taking sides with neither," as Delbrück put it, today's workers in the field are becoming increasingly conscious that what they are uncovering may well be directly applicable, and soon, to the control of virus-caused disease.

There are good pragmatic reasons for this attitude. The key to the chemical control of any parasite, whether a mouse in the kitchen, a weed in the lawn, a bacterium in the intestinal tract, or a virus in the cell, is to find and attack some key point of difference between the unwanted intruder and the host one is striving to preserve. The sulfonamides, for example, which were discovered in the 1930s, work because they closely resemble a compound called para aminobenzoic acid, PABA. PABA is used by bacteria to make folic acid, a vitamin. Because of this resemblance, the sulfonamides enter the bacterial cell's enzymatic machinery in the place of PABA and keep it from functioning. Since animal cells cannot make the vitamin anyway, they have other arrangements for acquiring folic acid and do not need PABA, so the bacterial cells are selectively destroyed.

RNA Viruses

At one time it was believed that the virus was almost totally dependent upon the facilities provided by its host, a situation that would make chemotherapy almost impossible. But it is now believed, partly by analogy with the bacteriophage, that although the animal virus does use the energy supplies of the host cell and depends upon it for the building blocks of nucleic acids and proteins, the virus also induces new enzymes and new functions that might provide vulnerable points for attack.

Among the most interesting recent studies of this sort are those carried out with the picorna viruses, in particular polio and Mengo, a mouse encephalitis agent. James Darnell of the Massachusetts Institute of Technology and Richard Franklin and David Baltimore, who worked together at The Rockefeller Institute, have been major contributors to these investigations.

The most intriguing feature of these viruses is the dual function of their nucleic acid. The great advances in molecular genetics of the last decade have spelled out the separate roles of DNA and RNA in the cell and documented them with painstaking detail. But in picorna-virus infected cells, the RNA is both messenger and the bearer of the genetic code. For a long time, biologists were reluctant to believe that RNA could violate the rules so flagrantly. Perhaps, they reasoned, the RNA might "turn on" a corresponding cellular DNA in the cell or cause one to be created, but although such a DNA was energetically sought, none was found. Then an antibiotic, Actinomycin D, was discovered to bind with the DNA molecule and inhibit both its replication and its production of RNA. In the uninfected cell, treatment with Actinomycin

D halts the formation of all new RNA, messenger, transfer, or ribosomal. But in the polio-infected cell, production of polio virus RNA, though of no other RNA, goes
ahead right on schedule. This RNA can replicate itself
with no help whatsoever from its so-called mother molecule.

Nor can its messenger function be doubted. Darnell,
using the cell-free *E. coli* system employed by Nirenberg
and Matthaei in their deciphering of the genetic code, has
been able to show that isolated strands of polio RNA, using the *E. coli* ribosomes and other equipment, will order
the synthesis of molecules of polio coat protein.

This unconventional RNA, which makes up about
twenty-five per cent by weight of each picorna virus particle, contains an estimated 6000 nucleotides—enough to
code some 2000 amino acids. Polio coat proteins contain
about 200 amino acids in each molecule, so even if two
kinds are involved, as some studies indicate, there is
enough information left over even in this small virus to
make several additional proteins, presumably the enzymes
involved in making more viruses.

Dulbecco and Vogt, using plating techniques, have
shown that a single particle is enough to set up an infection; in other words, just one of these RNA molecules is
enough to destroy a test tube full of cells, to kill a mouse,
or to cripple a child. So there is no division of labor among
a host of particles. One alone can do the trick. But, it has
also been shown, this particle must be intact. One of the
most perplexing problems of all about picorna virus infection is how in the hostile world of the cytoplasm, where
single strands of RNA—the messenger RNA's of the cell
—are ripped apart almost as rapidly as they are formed,
this single fragile deadly thread can manage to survive.

The most critical point in the life cycle would seem to
be that moment at which the information-laden molecule
slips free of its protein capsid. At that very instant it

must have to reach a ribosome, and it seems safe to assume that unless it manages to find one available and to attach itself very rapidly, the infection is aborted. Once attached, the RNA appears to serve as messenger RNA, dictating the production of enzymes, particularly those concerned with RNA replication.

Such an enzyme system, RNA polymerase, was recently demonstrated by Baltimore and Franklin. This enzyme system, in the presence of an intact strand of RNA, knits together a complementary strand of ribonucleotides, just as the enzyme discovered by Kornberg some years before links deoxyribonucleotides into DNA when a DNA template is there to copy. RNA polymerase differs from DNA polymerase in that it is never found in uninfected cells, or anywhere else in the world for that matter. Severo Ochoa has suggested that actually two enzymes are made, one which converts the single-stranded RNA to a double-stranded form and another which uses the double-stranded form as a template to produce more single strands, identical to the original.

After the new enzymes are made, RNA switches from the messenger to the genetic role and begins to replicate itself. Once this new viral RNA has begun to form, new messenger strands commandeer the ribosomes, often attaching to many of them simultaneously. At this stage, coat proteins are produced which finally coalesce and crystallize around an RNA molecule to form new particles.

About ten years ago at The Rockefeller Institute Igor Tamm began to look for chemicals that would inhibit the growth of viruses. He chose a group known as the benzimidazoles because they somewhat resembled vitamin B_{12} known to be needed for nucleic acid synthesis, and about all that was certain at that time about the replication of animal viruses was that nucleic acid synthesis was involved. Of this family, one, hydroxybenzylbenzimidazole, usefully abbreviated as HBB, has been found to be the most active.

HBB is highly specific, Tamm and his coworker Hans Eggers have discovered. It inhibits only picorna viruses and only certain ones of these, including polio and some of the ECHO and Coxsackie viruses, and it can entirely prevent multiplication of these viruses at concentrations which have no apparent effect on uninfected cells. And, as it turns out it seems to bear no relationship whatsoever to vitamin B_{12}.

In the HBB-treated cells, The Rockefeller Institute group has shown, the RNA polymerase does not appear, although if it is already present, the HBB will not stop it from acting. Because of its ability to distinguish one iso-lated function in one relatively small and closely related group of viruses, Tamm and Eggers believe that HBB must in some way "recognize" and interact with some very specific portion of the RNA molecule that is shared by certain close relatives of the picorna family. This is an exciting prospect to the biochemist because no compound with this sort of specificity has ever been found—and it would provide an exquisite probe for studying the fine structure of the virus gene.

HBB has not, however, proved useful in animals in-fected with picorna viruses. Even in the test tube, strains of virus that are resistant to its action arise rapidly and, curiously, strains have also appeared that cannot multi-ply at all unless HBB is present. Presumably it is the rapid development of resistance that enables the infection to escape HBB control. More recently, another com-pound, guanidine, has shown up in the course of a wide screening program for viral inhibitors carried out by Parke, Davis & Company. Guanidine, it has been found, also stops the production of RNA polymerase. However, it exerts its inhibiting effects on a slightly different though overlapping group of viruses. This leads Tamm and Eggers to believe that it acts somewhat differently biochemically, an hypothesis that is borne out by the fact that HBB and guanidine together, each in a half dose, are more effective than either alone in full dosage, and that one will act against strains that have become resistant to the other. It seems possible that combinations of the two may offer a useful approach to the chemotherapy of the picorna viruses. In any case, the RNA self-replicating system is clearly an ideal objective for chemotherapeutic attack and HBB and guanidine, although perhaps not the ultimate weapons, are helping to delineate that target.

DNA Viruses

In the case of the DNA viruses, it is proving more difficult to sort out their activities from those of the infected cells. Once Wyatt and Cohen discovered that the T-even phage contained a highly unusual DNA, they had a key to separating at least some of the enzyme systems of the virus from those of the host cell. No biological purpose has yet been found for the strange nucleic acid and one must suppress the thought that it evolved only for the purpose of giving sustenance to Cohen and Kornberg and their followers. No such obliging molecules have been found in any of the animal viruses and no enzymes have been set apart as being definitely viral in nature. Nonetheless, chemicals have been found that do stop virus growth, some of them without apparent harm to the host cell, and the very fact that such chemicals can be found establishes that there are fundamental differences, either quantitative or qualitative, that distinguish the biochemistry of the virus.

The first successful chemotherapy of a virus-caused disease occurred in 1962 with the use of one of a series of compounds that had been developed for the specific purpose of inhibiting DNA replication. In all of these compounds, the CH_3 group of atoms had been removed from the thymine molecule and replaced by a single atom of either chlorine, fluorine, bromine, or iodine. It was hoped in this way to interfere with the cell's use of thymine and so to repress specifically the biosynthesis of DNA—since thymine is needed for DNA and DNA alone. If cells could not make DNA, perhaps the rapid cellular proliferation of cancer cells might be stopped. The problem is, as was foreseeable from the beginning, that many other cells, those of the bone marrow and the lining of the intestinal tract, for example, also multiply rapidly and although the halogenated pyrimidines, as they are called, do slow cancer growth in some cases, they have proved damaging to normal tissues.

In the early 1960s, Herbert Kaufman, an ophthalmologist then at the Massachusetts Eye and Ear Infirmary, began to speculate on the possibility of using one of these compounds against herpes infection of the eye. These infections are fairly common, very painful, difficult to control, and may so scar the cornea that blindness results. Since they are localized, two major chemotherapeutic problems are obviated; first, the pure compound in high doses can be kept concentrated at the site of infection and, second, comparatively little reaches the rest of the body to damage other tissues. Kaufman selected one of the group, IUDR (iododexoyuridine), and tried it first in rabbits with experimental infections and subsequently in patients. About seventy-five per cent of those with acute infections and many with deep chronic inflammations have responded to the drug. The corneal cells grow and heal despite the IUDR treatments. The drug is now produced commercially and available in neighborhood drugstores.

Subsequently it was shown that IUDR is also active against herpes infections of the skin and that recurrences seem to occur less frequently following drug treatment. Because of this, it has been suggested that the strange pyrimidine may actually be incorporated into the viral DNA and so form a "pseudovirus" that cannot replicate itself.

In an attempt to assess the systemic effects of the drug, Paul Calabresi of Yale University Medical School sought out patients with advanced cancer who were being treated with IUDR and who had not been vaccinated against smallpox for twenty years or more. The vaccinia virus was unable to grow in these patients and no vaccination could be established. In cases in which vaccination was tried again after drug treatment had been discontinued, the vaccinations took. IUDR causes severe side effects and could probably only be used to stem a very dangerous infection, but its antiviral effects seem to be well established. Recently, Calabresi and Huebner tried giving IUDR to newborn hamsters treated with the cancer-causing adenoviruses. No tumors appeared in the treated animals.

A dramatic development in the prevention of virus diseases by chemotherapy occurred the following year, in 1963. The compound used was thiosemicarbazone, one of a group of chemicals that had been under study for almost a decade by D. J. Bauer and his colleagues at the Wellcome Foundation in England. It had been shown to inhibit the growth of vaccinia and smallpox viruses in the laboratory, and when a smallpox epidemic broke out in India—an epidemic made possible only by the public's failure to keep their vaccinations up to date—the authorities gave permission for a widespread trial of the drug. It turned out to be what the British medical journal, *Lancet*, not usually an overdemonstrative publication, said might be "the most significant advance in smallpox control since the days of Jenner."

The day after any smallpox patient was admitted to

the Infectious Diseases Hospital in Madras, a visit was paid to his house. Half of the persons with whom he lived were given a supply of the drug, with instructions for its use, and the other half were given a placebo or no drug. The fact that the compound can be given orally greatly facilitated this sort of mass distribution. Altogether, 1101 persons received the drug. Among these there were three cases of smallpox, all of which were mild, two of which occurred among patients who had received less than the recommended dosage. Among 1126 similarly exposed controls, seventy-eight developed smallpox and twelve died.

Thiosemicarbazone is not active against other groups of viruses, and the way it acts against smallpox and vaccinia is not entirely clear. Viral DNA and viral protein are formed in the infected cells, but they do not seem to come together to make complete virus particles, perhaps because the production of some assembling enzyme is blocked, or perhaps because some of the components are abnormal—simply the wrong shape perhaps—and so do not fit together properly. In any case, the compound seems to have little effect on the human body; the only troublesome side effect is occasional nausea. Its chief use, however, seems to be prophylactic.

Recently one more new compound has appeared on the horizon, amantadine hydrochloride, which appears to interfere with the penetration of host cells by some members of the myxo group. Amantadine hydrochloride, developed by DuPont, has been reported on the basis of trials in convicts to have some effects on preventing the spread of influenza. More recently, there have been reports that it may have some activity against German measles, one of the viral diseases for which an effective treatment would be most particularly welcome.

The chances are that all of these compounds, new though they are, will soon be superseded by others, perhaps now being tested in the laboratory. Perhaps the most important thing about them will turn out to be the stimulus they are imparting both to basic research and to experimental chemotherapy in this field. As studies of the life cycle of the virus progress parallel to the development of new compounds to check viral growth, it is really no longer possible, and certainly not very useful, to try any further to distinguish, in this particular area, the boundary separating the search for truth, so-called basic research, from the equally human desire to alleviate suffering and disease.

16 The Human Cancer Virus

Bernard Peyrilhe, professor at the Royal College of Surgeons in Paris, collected a few drops of fluid from the cancerous breast of one of his patients and inoculated it under the skin of a dog. The wound at the site of the inoculation became swollen and discolored until, at the end of five days, Peyrilhe's servant became so distressed at the howls of the animal that he drowned it. Peyrilhe, interpreting these results as proving that human cancer is caused by a "virus," reported them at the Academy of Sciences in Lyons in 1775 and received the prize for the best essay on the causes, nature, and prevention of cancer. Since that time, the problem has grown increasingly complex.

A century after Peyrilhe, in the early days of bacteriology, "causative" organisms—bacilli, cocci, fungi—were found time and again in cancer tissue; triumphant reports of their isolation issued forth, swelled and died, leaving only the mocking echoes. The rich, fulminating growth of cancer tissue, it now seems clear, provides a fertile soil for the propagation of a number of parasites, including viruses, which may or may not affect the course of the disease but certainly serve to obscure the explorations of its causes. The repeated failures of the work on bacterial transmission, coupled with the shameful treatment of patients by a medical profession and a general public that believed cancer to be contagious, led the entire subject of an infectious origin for the disease into total disrepute.

Throughout the subsequent years, a number of factors

were discovered to be involved with cancer development. Tars and other chemicals, ultraviolet light, X-rays, hormone imbalances, all were shown to "cause" cancer, at least in the laboratory and sometimes, according to the evidence, in man as well. But there were two problems. First, the great majority of human cancers could not be linked to any of these known agents. Secondly, the idea of multiple causation of cancer, while tenable, was not intellectually very satisfying. The idea evolved that cancer was perhaps a mutation of body cells, a change in the hereditary material of the cell that was passed on by cell division to innumerable daughter cells. This change in some unspecified way releases the cell from the restraints that control the growth of its normal relatives, it was proposed. This idea was supported by evidence that most of the agents that caused cancer—X-rays, ultraviolet irradiation, and many of the chemicals as well—caused mutations in the faithful fruitfly and other useful biologic systems.

As more and more animal cancers were found to be of viral origin, the notion of a human cancer virus became inescapable. As Enders has said, "It becomes increasingly unlikely that humans are exempt from the phenomenon which has now been evoked so easily and so often in a variety of other species." As early as 1957, Stanley, always the revolutionist, boldly stated that it was time to consider the possibility that not merely some but all human cancers were caused by viruses. Even earlier, in 1956, Duran-Reynals, in one of those quiet statements that cling curiously in the mind, pointed out: "There is no evidence whatsoever that carcinogenesis has ever been observed in the proven absence of viruses."

It is possible to build an attractive case for the theory that all cancers are caused by viruses, with factors in the external or internal environment previously considered cancer causes playing a secondary role. As long ago as

1938, Rous and his associate John G. Kidd showed that in rabbits with Shope papillomas, tar, injury, or bacterial infection could set off the change to cancer. Bittner in his studies on mouse mammary cancer clearly demonstrated that virus alone was not enough but that hormones, heredity, and time also played a role. When Miriam Lieberman and Henry S. Kaplan of Stanford University School of Medicine confirmed Gross's finding that a leukemia-causing virus could be isolated from mice in which the disease had been induced by X-rays, they concluded with the statement that the observation lends "new emphasis" to the view that all cancers result from "viruses or viruslike agents." In short, human cancer might be caused by some extremely common virus, as common as polyoma in mice, and the occurrence of cancer in the one in five who actually develop the disease is, as Gross puts it, "an unfortunate accident."

It is possible that there is no cancer virus in the specific sense, but that a number of common viruses may have this property. Duran-Reynals conducted a series of experiments, now being continued by his widow, Maria-Louisa, which showed that combinations of vaccinia virus and small amounts of carcinogenic tars produce cancers in mice far more often than the tars alone. Occasional reports have appeared of cancers arising in vaccination scars—although it should be remembered that all scar tissue is a favored site for cancer growth—and also in recurring fever blisters caused by herpes. Herpes, polio, and West Nile, an arbovirus, will increase the frequency of occurrence of cancers induced by carcinogenic tars. All of these observations are not out of keeping with the findings in animals in which almost every class of virus—pox, myxo, adeno, papova—has been shown to have some cancer-producing members. Hilleman says, "The most impressive qualities of the animal cancer viruses are their 'ordinariness!'" and Andrewes confirms, "It is apparent that tumors are not caused by viruses with unusual properties but as a result of a particular state of association between cells and viruses of quite different kinds. All sorts of viruses can become oncogenic."

But emphasis on viruses tends to overlook other new findings about cancer. One absolutely incontrovertible fact that has emerged from cancer research in the last decade is the association between cigarette smoking and cancer of the lung; it is possible to argue that the cigarette tar triggers a latent virus, but careful studies of the pathological stages in the development of lung cancer really do not seem to suggest the necessity for the intervention of any viral agent. Also, in another and almost equally interesting development—though not of such wide and immediate practical import—Peter C. Nowell of the University of Pennsylvania School of Medicine has discovered an abnormal chromosome, called the Philadelphia chromosome in honor of the city of its discovery, that is regularly associated with one type of chronic leukemia. This, of course, lends considerable substance to the so-called mutation theory.

Taking a broad view of the field, some authorities have come forward with what Frank Horsfall, director of the Sloan-Kettering Institute for Cancer Research, refers to as the "unifying theory" of cancer cause. The hereditary material of the cell is a nucleic acid. Changes in the nucleic acids are the underlying basis of mutations and also of cancer. The active component of viruses is also a nucleic acid. Adding the nucleic acid of a virus to the nucleic acid of a cell, it has been shown conclusively, can create a new cell with new properties, a cancer cell, but viruses, "transmissible mutagens," are just one of the many ways in which such cells can be created.

Other evidence indicates that the production of cancer may not be quite so exquisitely specific. The primary event in the development of cancer may be a disruption of the chromosome. X-rays cause visible breaks in the chromosome, as do some cancer-causing chemicals. SV40, polyoma, herpes, and the cancer-causing adenoviruses also cause chromosome upheavals. So does measles, an almost universal childhood infection which multiplies mainly in lymphoid tissues, the site of more than half of the cancers of childhood. Perhaps the general setting for the development of cancers is the disruption of the chromosomes. Out of this shamble of chromosomal aberrations, as Trentin puts it, there may arise from time to time the cancer cell.

The newest and most iconoclastic voices in the field at present are those who claim that there is actually no reason to believe either that all cancers arise from nuclear changes or that they are all caused by viruses. Rubin, for instance, points out that in his opinion the cancers resulting from Rous sarcoma infection might well result from changes in the cell membranes that release cells from the contact inhibition operative in normal cells, and that such changes in cell surface, no matter what their etiology, might be the common denominator, if there is one. Enders, on the other hand, suggests that cells have an inherent "potential" to become cancerous and that viruses merely exert a secondary effect by activating this pre-existent potential. As one authority in the field put it not long ago, "Everyone working with viruses and tumors is entitled to guess."

The Missing Protagonist

Recently in the midst of a seminar on quantum mechanics, a distinguished physicist stated that although it was not certain whether or not one long-sought type of elementary particle, the gravitron, actually exists, scientists were now prepared to define its properties. For somewhat similar reasons, this extremely provocative, rapidly unfolding drama of the human cancer viruses has been entitled by Koprowski: "Hamlet without the Prince of Denmark." In short, although all agree that a human cancer virus does probably exist, no one has yet demonstrated it.

There are many clues to the identity of the missing protagonist. In 1957 Leon Dmochowski of the University of Texas, in a review of the electron microscope studies of the newly isolated avian and mouse leukemia viruses, reported that he had found two very similar particles in the lymph nodes of patients with acute leukemia. These were in the same size range (700 to 1000 Angstroms) as the mouse leukemia viruses and had the same myxovirus-like features of a dense central area surrounded by one or two concentric membranes. Since that time there have been sporadic reports, occurring with increasing frequency, of similar particles found in some but not all leukemia patients. Among the most interesting are those isolated by Dalton and Moloney because they so strikingly resemble the Moloney leukemia virus of mice, which has been proved conclusively to cause the disease in that species.

A problem inherent in these studies is illustrated by the recent work of the Melnicks at the University of Texas, who have stressed that, "in any population of biological debris, a few particles can certainly be found that resemble the morphological irregular myxoviruses." In order to avoid this pitfall, they have not searched for single particles but have tried to follow a quantitative approach, which has been successful to the extent that large numbers of virus-like particles have been found more often in patients with leukemia. The particles isolated by the Melnicks also look like myxoviruses but appear to be somewhat larger than the known mouse leukemia agents or than the other virus-like particles found in human patients. Most disconcertingly, as the Melnicks have also reported, seemingly identical particles are released into the plasma from whole blood cells if one allows blood to stand at a cold temperature for forty-eight hours or longer or if one disrupts blood cells by alternate freezing and thawing. The Melnicks believe they are dealing with a virus, and the particles certainly look like viruses, but all agree that electron microscopy alone cannot offer unequivocal proof.

In 1945 J. B. Thiersch of Adelaide, Australia, in a large study involving some sixty human beings, took cell-free filtrate from the tissues of patients dying of leukemia and injected them into patients with other types of cancer and with various other chronic diseases, all of whom were in such an advanced stage of illness that they were not expected to live more than two years. Some of them did survive past their allotted time, but none of them developed new and different cancers. In the 1950s thousands of American schoolchildren were inoculated with SV40, the monkey virus that causes the tumors in baby mice and hamsters. No unusual incidence or types of cancers have been reported in this group. As a recent reviewer of the subject dryly remarked in recalling Thiersch's work, it is unlikely that this type of experiment will enjoy any greater degree of popularity in the future.

A more universally acceptable approach is to inject extracts from human cancers into laboratory animals, and, beginning with Peyrilhe, the most extensive and confusing reports in this field have involved such experiments. In the largest study so far reported, Alice Moore of the Sloan-Kettering Institute inoculated over 5000 newborn Swiss mice with filtrates of human tumors from Memorial Hospital patients. About three per cent of the mice developed cancers, as compared to slightly less than one per cent of control mice that were inoculated with filtrates from normal tissues, a difference which she does not feel to be statistically significant. Among mice that received filtrates from the tissues of patients with leukemias or lymphomas, about ten per cent developed cancer, a difference that would appear to have some meaning but it is difficult to interpret. In a similar large study, James Grace at the Roswell Park Memorial Institute in Buffalo injected extracts from over sixty malignant tumors and leukemias into 1397 newborn Swiss mice, of which about five per cent developed cancer.

It is important to point out that none of the cancers that developed in these animals bore any relationship to the type of human cancer from which the filtrate was prepared; they were all cancers of the type that these mice develop spontaneously. Moore, in reviewing her own results, suggests that there might be a virus in the filtrate that triggers a virus in the mouse. Or, in line with Rubin's findings on the defectiveness of the Rous sarcoma virus, one virus might "complete" another one. On the other hand, the human material might not contain any virus at all but merely serve in some way to lower the resistance of the animals to cancers that they otherwise would have been able to fend off successfully.

In a particularly bewildering series of investigations, mentioned previously, Schwartz and his coworkers have shown that filtrates of brain tissue of patients with leukemia will accelerate the rate of leukemia in a high leukemia strain of mice—in other words, mice that would probably have come down with leukemia anyway get it at an earlier age—and will also induce leukemia in Swiss mice which have a naturally low rate of the disease. No increase in leukemias results when extracts from the brains of patients who did not have leukemia are injected into the mice or when extracts are from the leukemic tissue themselves. Schwartz concludes that, in the first instance, no virus is present and, in the second, that there is something in the cancer that neutralizes the virus or interferes with its expression. No other investigators have yet confirmed Schwartz's work, which was first reported several years ago, but the story of Gross's long struggle for acceptance of the first mouse leukemia virus makes one hesitate to dismiss it on these grounds.

Shope, who has been active in the cancer virus field for some thirty years now, is of the opinion that it is quite unrealistic to expect that any tumor virus of man will exert its neoplastic effect in the mouse or the hamster or for that matter any other so-called lower animal. But there is a faint ray of hope in the fact that some cancer viruses do cross species lines. Years ago Duran-Reynals showed that the Rous virus could be transmitted to ducks and turkeys if young animals were used. Stewart found that polyoma crossed the species barriers to infect rats and hamsters as well as mice. Recently Chester Southam and J. Spencer Munroe of the Sloan-Kettering Institute have succeeded in producing sarcomas in rats and in monkeys with the Rous virus, crossing not only the species line but leaping the broader evolutionary gap separating bird and mammal. In 1964 Grace reported that a laboratory assistant working with the Yaba monkey tumor accidentally pricked his hand with a virus-infected needle and developed a tumor at the site of the injection. As in the monkey, the tumor proved benign and regressed spontaneously. But no virus has ever been isolated from a human cancer that has regularly and unequivocally caused a tumor in a laboratory test.

Tissue culture, which proved such a useful technique for tracking down the strains of polio and revealing the existence of the ECHO viruses, has been less helpful in the case of the cancer viruses. A. J. Girardi, one of Hilleman's associates in the tissue culture studies that uncovered SV40, has attempted to disclose viruses in more than 300 specimens of human cancers. He reported: "The present studies are remarkable for their failure." During 1964, there was a flurry of excitement when a number of investigators reported finding "viruses" in the blood or bone marrow of patients with leukemia which produced visible lesions, cytopathogenic effects, in embryonic cells growing in tissue culture. These effects subsequently proved to be caused by a type of very small bacteria known as PPLO (pleuropneumonia-like organism) which is only 1250 to 1500 Angstroms in diameter. Although smaller than the large viruses, PPLO is definitely not a virus; it can live outside a living cell and reproduces by cell division. Unlike most bacteria, however, it has a protozoa-like flexible cell wall so it can take many forms and closely mimic the contours of the rather shapeless myxoviruses.

PPLO, of which some thirty strains have been identified, is known to cause a variety of diseases in farm animals and a form of pneumonia in man. They are a common contaminant of sewage, garbage, and, also, it now seems, of tissue cultures. Some investigators have tentatively put forth the suggestion that the association between human cancers and PPLO may be more than coincidental, but this has not been proved. In any case, PPLO seriously dashed the hopes of a number of workers who believed that they had at last found the elusive cancer virus.

One of the conventionally most useful ways of tracking viruses is, of course, by their antibodies. Viruses such as SV40 and polyoma not only leave a trail of antibodies to the virus itself but also apparently antibodies characteristic for the cancer cells that they cause, and similarly cancer caused by the adenoviruses and the leukemia viruses contain a viral antigen even though the virus itself is nowhere to be found. Whether or not this same condition would obtain in the case of the hypothetical human cancer virus is of course not known. Schwartz, for instance, finds that the blood of leukemia patients does not have any neutralizing effect on the leukemia virus he has isolated in the mice. On the other hand, blood of persons

who have been in close contact with the leukemia patient
may have such a neutralizing effect. The patients, he reasons, develop their disease because of their lack of resistance; this would result in a situation rather like that
of a detective trying to convict a suspect on the basis of
the absence of his particular fingerprints. Similarly if Gross
is right and human leukemia, like mouse leukemia and
chick leukemia, is passed "vertically," that is, from mother
to offspring yet unborn, one would not necessarily expect
to have antibodies against it.

Leukemia in Niles

In February 1961, Sister Mary Viva, principal of the St.
John Brebeur School in Niles, Illinois, wrote a letter to
the executive director of the American Cancer Society's
Illinois division reporting "an unusual number of deaths
of children from leukemia," and set off a series of investigations and a controversy that has not yet subsided. Between 1957 and 1960, as it turned out, there had actually
been eight cases of leukemia. Eight cases is not precisely
an epidemic, although that word was used from time to
time in the more dramatic accounts of this study, but it
was about four times as many cases of leukemia as Niles,
a town of less than 20,000 inhabitants, would have been
expected to have in that length of time. Students of
probability know that it is not unusual for chance events
to distribute themselves in such an uneven fashion. Further investigation made it less simple to dismiss the findings on those grounds. There was no direct contact among
these children, but the community Catholic school was
attended by three of these children, although none of
them were in the same class, and by the healthy older
brothers and sisters of four others. This does not of course
prove the leukemias were caused by an infectious agent
or a virus, and it could still all be a coincidence, but one

is left with the uneasy feeling that there was something special going on in that community that was somehow involved with children and with their deaths.

The Niles incident spurred reviews of epidemiological studies of childhood leukemia and sparked some additional ones. Despite the curious proximity of those particular eight patients, leukemia certainly does not appear to be contagious in any ordinary sense of the word. Of several hundred women with leukemia during pregnancy, only one has been described as having a child with leukemia. Conversely, the frequency of leukemia among mothers whose children develop leukemia does not seem to exceed normal expectations. When an identical twin develops leukemia, there is a one-to-five chance that his cotwin will develop it within a few months, but no such correspondence exists for fraternal twins. Broad surveys of the incidence of leukemia reveal little or no tendency for it to occur in clusters. Some studies have indicated that leukemia is more likely to occur at certain times of the year, the summer in England, the winter and spring in the United States, for example. Most investigators feel that these differences, which are slight at best, are not very meaningful, since it is difficult to say exactly when a case of leukemia actually begins. Nor is the fact that leukemia is seasonal actually a strong indication of its viral nature.

The African Lymphoma

In 1958 Dennis Burkitt, a missionary surgeon in the city of Kampala in Uganda, began a study of a peculiar, highly characteristic cancer of the jaw seen among children of the region. The cancer was not new—convincing descriptions of the hideous growth are found in the notes of Sir Albert Book, a missionary doctor who worked in Africa at the turn of the century—but only a few such cancers have been seen on other continents. Pathologic examination of the tumor tissue showed that it was actually a lymphoma, a cancer of the blood-forming tissues, which, in these cases, appeared to arise from the marrow of the jawbone. Following this clue, he discovered that a large variety of hitherto unrelated cancers among the children—cancers of the kidneys, ovaries, stomach, intestines—were all actually this same sort of cancer. They are "appallingly malignant," in the words of the pathologist J. N. P. Davies of Makerere College in Kampala, who worked with Burkitt on the study, and the children die within six to twelve weeks after the first symptoms appear.

Burkitt consulted the data of the Kampala Cancer Registry, sent a medical questionnaire to most of the large hospitals and clinics in Africa, and also went on a number of personal safaris into Central, West, and Southern Africa, inquiring about the incidence of the jaw tumors and other lymphomas. These statistics confirmed that the disease was indeed a common one, much the most common of all childhood cancers on the continent, and that it was particularly a disease of childhood; of the 260 patients studied in Burkitt's first series, 243 were between the ages of five and fourteen. It was not a cancer of African children, however, but distinctly a cancer of children in Africa, since it was also seen among the Indian, British, Lebanese, Syrian, and half-castes living in the country.

Burkitt and Davies, on the basis of their own data and that from the other medical centers, drew up a distribution map of the disease. The malignant lymphoma, the map showed, was distributed from coast to coast of Central Africa, with a strip running down the northeastern boundary toward South Africa. But the map, as plotted, had some holes or cancer-free areas in it. When it was shown to Sandy Haddow, director of the Virus Research Institute at the nearby township of Entebbe, he pointed out that the disease was found in the tropical and subtropical regions around the valleys and lakes but not in the deserts and highlands. More specifically, it was found in areas in which the average temperature did not fall below sixty degrees and where the rainfall is more than twenty inches a year, although there are a few exceptions. The distribution of yellow fever follows the same pattern. In other words, the African lymphoma is found in mosquito country. The few adults in whom the lymphoma has been seen all have been newcomers to these areas. More recently, the lymphoma has also been reported from New Guinea, which has much of the same flora and fauna as tropical Africa.

Burkitt suggests that the virus, if it is a virus, might be borne by some jungle insect to which children might not be exposed until they begin to range away from their homes, at the age of about five, and that the infection might be a common one, but the cancer a rare manifestation of it, much rarer for instance than paralysis in polio.

Dalldorf, who has spent much time in Africa recently, points out that in the areas in which the malignant lymphomas are seen, acute leukemias, the most common cancer among children in most other countries, are very rare. The higher the incidence of lymphoma, the lower the incidence of leukemia, but when the two are added together, their combined incidence, regardless of continent, is the same. Furthermore, the marrow cells in Burkitt's lymphoma resemble the cells of certain types of leukemia. So perhaps, Dalldorf proposes, it is really all the same disease with the same cause but different modifying factors—malaria, for instance, is known to change the immune responses of the host—and perhaps it is that modifying factor, not the agent of the lymphoma, that is peculiar to Africa.

At this point, there seems little room left for serious doubt that some human cancers, like so many animal cancers, are the result of virus infections. It is highly probable that some of these viruses have already been isolated and are captive in the laboratory. Whether or not they can be proved to cause the disease in the strictly dogmatic sense is not yet clear; it may just be that the entire question will be pushed aside by the sheer weight of circumstantial evidence. As the evidence accumulates, one sometimes gets the feeling that once the guilty particle is triumphantly held aloft, cancer, so old and so ugly, will flee the land. One can only hope that this is true. But, in any case, and at the very least, it would mean the long discouraging effort to understand cancer and to find new means for its control will be swept forward in the rapidly flowing current of modern virology.

17   The Man-made Future

About three billion years ago, the gases of the primitive atmosphere were torn apart, perhaps by lightning, the sun's radiant energy, or the volcanic heat from under the crust of the earth. Atoms reassembled themselves and new molecules were formed, destroyed, formed again until finally life flickered, clung, and managed to sustain itself. A chance combination of chemicals had taken place that had the power of self-replication. It is not known how many experiments failed, how many different kinds of living systems, once set forth, survived for a time and then sputtered out. Apparently only one succeeded, however, at least on this particular planet.

It is now clear from what is known of its expressions that the genetic code is universal. The protein-translating systems of bacterial cells can "read," with almost equal facility, the infectious nucleic acid of polio, of tobacco mosaic virus or, as experiments in Fritz Lipmann's laboratory at The Rockefeller Institute have shown, the messenger RNA from cells of the rabbit. The enzyme systems of *Homo sapiens* are little different from those of the red bread mold *Neurospora crassa*. So the slender thread of DNA links us not only to our parents and their forefathers but to the simplest of single cells and to their even more venerable ancestors. There are differences, of course—biochemical variations by which the experts are now learning to trace the intricate byways of evolution, but the essential sameness is what is strikingly clear. A populace which only a century ago strove to reject the fearful implications of familial ties with other primates is

now learning to accept—and with due reverence—that
E. coli is our cousin.

Implicit in this view of things is a glimpse of our own
impermanence. The cruel, chaotic, marvelous experiment
of evolution did not stop when Darwin flashed his light
upon it over a hundred years ago. It continues still, and
biological knowledge and the uses that are made of it must
be evaluated by us, the newcomers, in this perspective of
the endless continuum of time and of change.

Men and viruses are caught forever in this flux. In the
case of the latter, the evolutionary flow is rapid. Because
of the simplicity of their genetic make-up, viruses are able
to change and adapt very quickly. This is the attribute
that makes possible the deliberately attenuated strains
that serve as the vaccines for yellow fever, polio, and
measles. Similar adaptive changes take place also in the
world outside the laboratory. Influenza shifts with every
season, continually slipping through the immunological
nets. The flu of the twentieth century, the greatest of the
plagues, is clearly more virulent than the gentle "influ-
ences" of earlier days. With other viruses, natural selection may work toward a milder form of the disease. The
virus of myxomatosis as originally introduced into Australia was so rapidly fatal that the hideously ill animals
often did not have time to infect others before they died,
and so virus and host perished together. Those strains
which the luck of chance mutation turned away from
virulence had a better chance of reaching a new host and
so tended to survive. Within a year the fatality rate from
myxomatosis among the wild Australian conies had
fallen from more than ninety-nine per cent to ninety per
cent. That this actually represented a change in the virus
rather than the host was confirmed by injecting the newly
evolved strains into European rabbits and demonstrating
that this virus was indeed less virulent than the original
even for previously unexposed stock. Within a decade,

however, rabbits began to appear that were genetically resistant to myxomatosis and, although the disease still spreads, virus and rabbit have mutually accommodated themselves. Now the mortality has decreased to twenty-five per cent, and the rabbits have resumed their pillage of the Australian farms.

At one time biologists considered that life might have originated with the viruses, since these seemed to represent living in its simplest form. Today most who venture to speculate on such matters agree that viruses are rather degradative forms of more complicated organisms, creatures that have become increasingly simple rather than increasingly complicated. Work such as Campbell's on the F factor and the lambda phage, both of which may be part of the chromosome or exist separately from it, strongly suggests that, at least in bacteria, chromosomal fragments may break away and set up a more or less independent existence either as episomes or, if they acquire the ability to direct the production of protein vehicles, as viruses. Recently Riley, in an attempt to elucidate the size and structure of his LDH-elevating virus (the one that elevates the blood enzymes in mice), has found the particles isolated from the blood streams of the animals come in two sizes: one is conventional in its dimensions but the other, disconcertingly, seems to be something less than 100 Angstroms in diameter. This is smaller than any calculated theoretical lower limits for a virus, if one defines a virus, following Lwoff's generally accepted proposition, as RNA or DNA enclosed in protein. It appears as if at least this particular virus may exist in nature both with and without its protein capsid, with the free nucleic acid, if this is what it is, perhaps assuming some special form to escape the destructive enzymes of the blood stream. If this proves to be the case, it would lend support to current hypotheses, as yet only speculative, that cells—both single cells and those that compose the tissue of complex organisms—may exchange genetic messages in the form of free nucleic acid and that such exchanges may have important physiological consequences, such as, for example, a role in embryonic development. Under such conditions, it will be difficult to draw the line between transforming factors, viruses, extrachromosomal genes, and indeed the genes of the chromosomes themselves—all the bearers of an infectious heredity. So viruses not only change but, it seems possible, new viruses may be constantly generated, perhaps, one might even say, spontaneously.

Of course, from a different viewpoint, the whole pattern of disease is changing. The great killers of the last century were infections, like tuberculosis, pneumonia, and typhoid fever. Public sanitation, improved nutrition, and the advent of the modern antibiotics altered this picture to create, in the words of René Dubos, a new "mirage of health." Poliomyelitis is a twentieth-century disease, brought about by modern plumbing. Similarly, the modern hospital, which eliminated childbed fever, spawned the resistant staphylococci. The very lengthening of the life span—which stretched an average of some twenty years just between 1900 and 1950—itself greatly increased the prevalence of the degenerative diseases of the heart and blood vessels, cancer, and the other so-called chronic disorders of old age.

New disease patterns are emerging also among the young. Whooping cough, diphtheria, and infant diarrhea have virtually disappeared from modern America; cancer, unheard of in children a few decades ago, is now the major cause of childhood death from disease, with acute leukemia accounting for almost half the cases. The incidence of leukemia has increased somewhat in recent years and diagnostic acumen has improved greatly, but for the most part cancer looms to this grim prominence simply because the tide of infectious diseases has receded.

As man changes his relationships with disease, he may

alter the course of evolution. Persons who are heterozygous for the "molecular disease" of sickle cell anemia have been shown to be unusually resistant to malaria. As malaria ceases to reign over the equator, natural selection will cease to favor this potentially fatal disease. However, as many viewers-with-alarm among the eugenists have pointed out, man's increasing control over disease is actually running counter to the sort of eugenics practiced by the breeders, for instance, of poultry or prize cattle. Little more than forty years ago, the infantile diabetic died before he reached puberty. Today he can marry and have children and by so doing he returns his genes to the genetic pool. Similarly modern medical care is preserving the genomes of patients with "inborn errors of metabolism," such as cystic fibrosis and phenylketonuria, and in this generation, for the first time in man's history, some of these children will grow up to have children of their own.

Man's ability to tamper with the forces of natural selection renders him unique among other living creatures. Up until now, the nature of this tampering has been relatively unsophisticated, the introduction of the starling to North America, the explosion of a bomb at Alamogordo, the administration of insulin to a child. The genetic or ecological changes these produce, though implacable, are relatively slow, clumsy, and depersonalized. Now, however, modern biologists are coming close to the point at which they will be able to alter the genetic material at first hand. The next step in molecular genetics—and it may happen at any moment now—is the establishment of what the scientists term "colinearity," the matching of a cistron of DNA or its RNA messenger with the corresponding protein chain, the biological Rosetta stone. There are several different ways of working on this problem. George Streisinger in Hershey's laboratory at Cold Spring Harbor has been analyzing the fine structure of the gene of T4 that produces lysozyme, using Benzer's imaginative techniques. Streisinger has developed a series of mutant viruses, each of which produces a slightly different enzyme. By mapping the fine structure of the gene and analyzing the types and locations of the mutations within it, he may be able to make deductions about the sequence of nucleotide pairs. Fortunately this enzyme, which was isolated in 1958, is a relatively small protein, composed of only 156 different amino acids, the sequence of which is almost elucidated. So it may be possible, working back from the protein and the changes in it following specific mutations, to establish fairly clearly many details of the composition of the corresponding DNA. Using somewhat similar methods, Heinz Fraenkel-Conrat has been producing artificial changes in the RNA of tobacco mosaic virus and analyzing the subsequent changes in the coat protein of the TMV. This coat protein is made up of 158 amino acids, the sequence of which Fraenkel-Conrat has now elucidated.

Norton Zinder of The Rockefeller Institute and co-discoverer of viral transduction is approaching the same problem somewhat differently, using an *E. coli* bacteriophage which he and coworkers discovered in 1961. This phage, which bears the modest name f2, has two unusual and useful properties. First, it is an RNA virus, the first such bacteriophage to be found. Second, it is extremely small, only about 200 Angstroms in diameter, little larger than a molecule of hemoglobin. Zinder and his coworkers have calculated that the RNA of this phage contains only 2000 to 3000 nucleotides. According to present concepts, this could determine the sequence of only 700 to 1000 amino acids, in other words, only three or four proteins. One of these proteins, they have shown, is the coat protein. The isolated RNA of phage can function as messenger in cell-free extracts of *E. coli* and in these cell-free extracts to which the f2 RNA has been added, traces of newly formed f2 coat protein can be found. A second protein would appear to be RNA polymerase, the enzyme which is uniquely required by the RNA viruses for their unique function of RNA replication. RNA polymerase has been found in f2 infected cells. As Zinder says, all a virus really has to do is to get in, make more RNA and protein, and to get out again, which in theory should make detection of the remaining products of virus infection relatively simple, although in practice they are proving elusive. Fortunately, f2 is surprisingly easy to grow; a single infected bacterial cell yields 20,000 new particles within less than an hour, ten to twenty milligrams per liter of bacteria, a wealth of material with which to work.

In 1965 a team of scientists headed by Robert W. Holley of Cornell University worked out the nucleotide sequence of a molecule of transfer RNA. This is a relatively small molecule—only seventy-seven nucleotides in length as it turned out—compared to even the smallest messenger RNA's which have been estimated to start at 1200 nucleotides. Nevertheless, the methods used by Holley and his group are applicable to the larger molecules, and this achievement surely marks the beginning of similar studies on other, more complex, nucleic acids.

The recent reports of H. Gobind Khorana at the University of Wisconsin illustrate a third approach to the problem of colinearity. Khorana has recently devised techniques for synthesizing small DNA molecules with a predetermined sequence of purines and pyrimidines by adding deoxyribonucleotides one at a time to a stabilized growing chain. These small DNA models of known base sequence are limited to some fifteen or twenty nucleotides in length, but early reports suggest that they have biological activity; that is, supplied with Kornberg's enzyme system, they are self-replicating, and in the cell-free system of E. coli, they can direct the formation of polypeptides.

These synthetic molecules would thus provide a means for testing the present hypothesis about the details of the genetic code and perhaps throw some light on such questions as its punctuation.

These studies point, of course, toward the day when the scientist may be able to fabricate his own biologically active genetic material, in a sense, his own viruses. Manmade viruses might prove extremely useful, on one level, for stimulating or mobilizing immunological defenses. Their more important role would be their function as messengers, as augmenters of the genetic information of the genetically deficient cell. In 1959, not long before his death, Rivers, then medical director for the National Foundation, said, "Much if not all of mankind's illness is due to sick cells and much of this sickness is due to nucleic acid having gone bad. It is not too much to hope that some day man will be able to manipulate the nucleic acid in whole cells in intact living bodies in such a manner that much suffering, sickness, disability and mental illness will be prevented or alleviated." In 1960 Nobel laureate Edward Tatum spoke along these same lines: "With increased knowledge of the finer details of DNA and of the code relating one to the other, it may eventually be possible to synthesize better DNA and genes and hence proteins and other enzymes to order. This would be the ultimate in 'biological engineering'."

In 1962, Waclaw Szybalski and his wife, working at the University of Wisconsin, reported that they had isolated DNA from human bone marrow cells growing in tissue culture and had added this DNA to a colony of mutant human cells which lacked the ability to synthesize a particular enzyme. This DNA imparted to the mutant cells, and to their descendants, the ability to direct production of the lacking enzyme. In other words—and for the first time—the transformation of a human cell was effected.

Knowledge and Power

As the naturalist Joseph Wood Krutch has recalled, the inventor of an airplane in Samuel Johnson's *Rasselas* refused to make his invention public because he believed that not until man had first become virtuous should he be permitted to fly. Nevertheless, we are now flying, to the moon and beyond.

The next great problems in molecular genetics, as Tatum puts it, will be ethical ones.

The two themes of this book have been man's desire to know and his desire to use knowledge in useful or powerful ways. These are the two great currents of all science. At certain moments in history, new knowledge makes possible new and extraordinary powers, and at these moments the two currents fuse. Such a fusion took place a century ago in the imaginative genius of a single man, Pasteur, which is where this story began. From this fusion came man's ability, still very new, to alter significantly the course of human disease. A scant twenty-five years ago, another such fusion took place and we gained the power to destroy ourselves and, from time to time since then, have seemed very likely to use it.

Now, once again, it would seem that man's desire to know is leading him to a point at which he will possess great power. Hopefully this power will be used with reverence and humility. The "secret of life" is far more than the deciphering of a tetranucleotide code, as fascinating as this deciphering may be, just as man is more, as Theodosius Dobzhansky points out, than DNA's way of making more DNA. Life involves a complex interplay and modulation of many forces. It might be easy to pull a single thread in this grand fabric and mar the whole design.

The special gift that evolution has bestowed upon mankind is not only his ability to know and modify the world around him, but his sense of wonder and of awe, each hopefully balancing the other.

SUGGESTED READING

For those who are interested in reading further on this subject, I would like to recommend:

Viral and Rickettsial Infections of Man, J. B. Lippincott, 1965, edited by Frank L. Horsfall, Jr. and Igor Tamm, which is the fourth edition of the monumental work begun by Thomas Rivers;

Selected Papers on Virology, Prentice-Hall, Inc., edited by Nicholas Hahon, which is a collection of classic papers on the subject from 1798 to 1962;

the *Cold Spring Harbor Symposia on Quantitative Biology* for 1962 and 1963;

Advances in Virus Research, published annually by the Academic Press;

Viruses and the Nature of Life, E. P. Dutton, 1961, by Wendell Stanley and Evan G. Valens;

and numerous articles, past and future, in the *Scientific American*.

Index

HELENA CURTIS is a free-lance science writer whose work has appeared in *The Rockefeller Institute Review*, the *American Scientist*, and the *Sloan-Kettering Institute Progress Reports*, one of which formed the basis for this book. In 1963, she was awarded a Sloan-Rockefeller Advanced Science Writing Fellowship at Columbia University.

K3